THE MAKING OF PHYSICISTS

THE MAKING OF PHYSICISTS

edited by

Rajkumari Williamson

Department of History of Science and Technology, UMIST

Adam Hilger, Bristol

British Library Cataloguing in Publication Data

The Making of physicists.
  1. Physics—Study and teaching (Higher)
    —Europe—History—20th century
  I. Williamson, Rajkumari
  530'.07'114   QC47.E85

ISBN 0-85274-524-9

Published under the Adam Hilger imprint by IOP Publishing Ltd
Techno House, Redcliffe Way, Bristol BS1 6NX, England

Printed in Great Britain by J W Arrowsmith Ltd, Bristol

Contents

PREFACE

This book contains personal accounts by eighteen senior physicists of their undergraduate and postgraduate days in the inter-war period (1918–39). It is hoped that these narratives will illuminate the teaching and research pursuits of physics in a period when not only was physics undergoing some remarkable changes, but also the revolutionary ideas of the first two decades of this century were finding their way into the teaching syllabus. The authors were asked to include comments on:

(i) How good were their mentors as teachers?
(ii) What features of the undergraduate laboratory experiments and lecture syllabus do they particularly remember?
(iii) Did work for a research degree differ greatly then from what is expected today?
(iv) How and when did the new ideas and developments in physics (such as quantum mechanics, relativity, the nuclear atom, subatomic particles, etc) find their way into the syllabus?

Much has been written about the development of twentieth century physics and its concepts, but not enough about the teaching and the introduction of the new physics to students—who make up the succeeding generation of physicists. This book should fill this gap and perhaps provide stimulus to further research in this field.

A one-day symposium entitled 'The Education of Physicists Between the Wars' was organised by the History of Physics Group of The Institute of Physics on 30 October 1985 at the Greater Manchester Museum of Science and Industry. The talks given by six senior physicists to this gathering of physicists and science historians form part of the book.

The contributions are arranged chronologically in accordance with dates of entry of the authors to university. While some of the authors received their student training on the continent, all have made their subsequent careers in Britain or Ireland.

Of the many physicists invited to contribute, we are fortunate that those who were able to share their experiences give a representative coverage of the period. Their generous provision of photographs, student notebooks and examination papers has enhanced the text. It is a pleasure to acknowledge the help of the Archivists of the Universities

Figure 1   Speakers at the History of Physics Group meeting of 30 October 1985 held at The Greater Manchester Museum of Science and Industry: (left to right) Professors Burcham, Allibone, Sir Nevill Mott, Kurti, Sir Samuel Curran and Lipson. (Courtesy of The Greater Manchester Museum of Science and Industry.)

of Cambridge, Liverpool and Manchester and of the Librarian of the University of Bristol. I am indebted to Professor I S Hughes and his staff at the University of Glasgow and Dr J Muir and his colleagues at the University of Edinburgh for their help. Dr Stella Butler of the Museum of Science and Industry, Professor P G Murphy and Mr John Turner from the Schuster Laboratories of the University of Manchester made vital contributions to the success of the Manchester meeting. Professor A J Meadows and Dr J Roche of the History of Physics Group have given invaluable counsel and encouragement. I thank Mr J Marsh from the Department of History of Science and Technology, UMIST, for his unfailing help. Mr N Hankins of Adam Hilger originated the idea which led to this publication; I am grateful for his continued support.

This volume would not have been possible without the stimulating enthusiasm and energetic response of all the authors.

It was sad to hear of Professor Ditchburn's death while the book was in preparation; he gave me ready help, with careful attention to detail.

R Williamson

INTRODUCTION

R Williamson

We may make such words when they are wanted. As we cannot use 'Physician' for a cultivator of Physics, I have called him a Physicist. We need very much a name to describe a cultivator of science in general. I should incline to call him a Scientist.

William Whewell (1840)

At the beginning of the inter-war period the route to becoming a physicist was the well-established one of structured study for a prescribed number of years at a recognised institution. (A caveat must be made here—most general statements will refer to British institutions.)

The role of printed examination papers requiring written answers, in determining suitability for entry to a course, eligibility for a scholarship or for testing a corpus of knowledge acquired over a period, was well established and universally accepted. The other important element in the pedagogy of physics—laboratory instruction—was by this time an essential feature of the course.[1] Suitable degrees or diplomas were conferred upon those who satisfied the criteria.

The definition of theoretical physics (earlier mathematical physics) had slowly changed from being a subdivision which circumscribed a few particular topics to that of approach and application in the whole field of physics. Here there were many national and institutional differences in the mode and timing of its teaching.[2] In many instances a formal training in mathematics would form a route to physics.[3]

All this may now appear to be emphasising the obvious but the system designed to make physicists through mass education along the lines now so familiar to us had evolved over many decades and through the efforts of numerous individuals. Truisms of today were struggling truths expressed as perorations by the advocates of science and education in styles and metaphors characteristic of the individual or of the times.[4] This book does not attempt to trace this evolution; interesting and

1

worthy works on this subject already exist.[5] Here the story of this continuing change is taken up from after World War I and traced through
the personal experiences of many physicists. This collection may not
generate many statistics; it does not aim to do so. It does, however,
paint a vivid picture of a life of study in a variety of institutions, some
aspects of which will strike a familiar chord with many a student—past
or present.

In the first half of the nineteenth century physics had gradually carved
out a territory within natural philosophy and away from chemistry.[6] By
the end of the century it had acquired a separate identity as a discipline,
in spite of dangers of mergers with engineering or mathematics at times
of economic retrenchment. In the wake of this specialisation the
amateur scientist, the 'Gentleman of Science' and self-taught natural
philosophers like Joule were becoming an extinct species. Arthur
Schuster lamented their passing in his Presidential address to the British
Association in 1892, '... the gradual disappearance of the amateur may
be a necessary consequence of our increased educational facilities'. Gone
were the days when someone like Coleridge could say that he attended
Humphry Davy's lectures to increase his stock of metaphors!

An important factor in the proliferation of science in Britain was the
establishment of provincial University Colleges from 1870 onwards.
When many of these were granted autonomous university status in the
first decade of this century, it swelled the pool of science graduates from
2000 to 8000 between 1902 and 1914. This period also saw a boom
in the building of physics laboratories, e.g Manchester (1900),
Liverpool (1904), Birmingham (1905), Edinburgh (1907), Glasgow
(1908), Cardiff (1908), Oxford (1910), Dundee (1911) and the Royal
College of Science (1907). Many were substantially endowed by private
benefaction. The 1902 Education Act had set in motion the long
overdue reform of secondary education in Britain[7], providing thereby
the vital antecedent to university education. Thus, most of the apparent
desiderata for the successful training of physicists seemed to be realised.
However, for jobs in science-based industries for physics (and science)
graduates a yawning gap remained between expectations and
opportunities.[8]

Of this situation Kathleen Chorley says in her autobiography (1950),
'Today, "the application of science in industry" is a creed, in my
youth (1920s) it was a slogan, in father's youth it was a daring and
revolutionary conception.'[9]

The results of such neglect were brought into sharp focus through
shortages during World War I of materials traditionally imported from
Germany, such as dyestuffs, pharmaceuticals, magnetos and optical
glass. The exigencies of war led to the setting up of the Department of
Scientific and Industrial Research (DSIR) in 1916.[10] Its awards of

maintenance allowance for postgraduate students in training did facilitate research for many physicists in the inter-war period.

Post-war conditions provided further opportunities for change. The Fisher Education Act of 1918 raised the school leaving age to 14 and modifications of the secondary education system continued throughout the decade, despite the financial strictures of 1922 known as the 'Geddes-Axe'. The PhD degree was instituted in British universities with a view to attracting American and other overseas students, who would otherwise have gone to Germany for such qualifications. In the event, it was predominantly British students who gained PhDs in this period. Government schemes of higher education for returning soldiers and naval officers, celebrated so poignantly by Kipling in *The Scholars*, stretched the universities' resources; it also profoundly altered the social and cultural norms of student life; a 'plague of dancing' among the students was reported at the University of Sheffield.[11] Professor Allibone, in his contribution, gives a first-hand account of those days. The older universities of Oxford and Cambridge eventually admitted women to their degrees.[12]

The *ancien régime* was altering in many physics departments after the war. Rutherford moved from Manchester in 1919 to succeed Sir J J Thomson to the Cavendish Chair of Experimental Physics at Cambridge, which the latter had occupied since 1884. Rutherford in turn was succeeded by W L Bragg to the Langworthy Chair of Physics at Manchester. F A Lindemann was elected to the Chair of Experimental Philosophy at Oxford in 1919, in succession to R B Clifton who had been appointed to it in 1865. A Tyndall was appointed H O Wills Professor of Physics at Bristol in 1919. R Whiddington was appointed to the Cavendish Chair of Physics at Leeds, which had lain vacant for four years after W H Bragg's departure in 1915. S R Milner succeeded W M Hicks at Sheffield, whose incumbency had lasted from 1883 to 1917.

Certain events which proved to be of significance for the physics community in this period were taking place on the continent; The Niels Bohr Institute in Copenhagen was inaugurated on 3 March 1921[13]; Max Born moved to Göttingen in 1921 as the Director of the Institute for Theoretical Physics and persuaded James Franck to come there as the Director of the Second Physical Institute. Sir Nevill Mott and Lady Jeffreys describe their experiences at these Institutions respectively.

In spite of a promising early start, the hopes of a 'land fit for heroes' did not materialise for the victorious nations and the economic conditions were even worse for the vanquished. Severe unemployment in Europe, run-away inflation in Germany, a general strike in Britain and finally a depression marked the end of a turbulent decade. This was followed by the rise of Hitler and the expulsion of many academics from Germany from 1933 onwards.[14] These conditions form the backdrop to the student life of the authors—certainly no halcyon days of youth that exist in the popular imagination. However, even though conditions were austere and careers insecure, physics itself was embarking on a very exciting phase. New avenues of research were opening up, thus providing opportunities, satisfaction and camaraderie to many workers; perhaps enabling them to shut out the tumult of the outside world.

Science has its Cathedrals, built by the efforts of a few architects and of many workers.

G N Lewis and M Randall (*Thermodynamics*, 1923)

This was truly the age of the *atom*. Most of the sceptics had died (the chief amongst these, E Mach, died in 1916) and for any that remained J Perrin had laid down all the proofs for the existence of atoms in *Les Atomes* (1921). In fact, there was an essential continuity with the pre-war era and atomic models had proliferated in embarrassing numbers.[15] The Rutherford–Bohr model—a creation of the collective inspiration of the Manchester school just before the war—had emerged as the winner.[16] Its dramatic success in explaining spectroscopic data had in turn given fresh life and impetus to researches in spectroscopy. A healthy see-saw between theory and experiment in this field soon led to refinement of optical instruments and measurements on the one hand and to new insights into the structure of atoms and their periodic classification on the other, e.g. nuclear spin, Pauli's exclusion principle (1925) and electron spin (Goudsmit and Uhlenbeck 1925). It also gradually revealed the inadequacy of semiclassical models and of the use made of the correspondence principle.

Heisenberg, while working at Göttingen and later at the Niels Bohr Institute seeking 'to establish a basis for theoretical quantum mechanics founded exclusively upon relationships between quantities which in principle are observable', introduced a new kind of kinematics in 1925. Max Born soon recognised it as such and with the help of P Jordan formulated Heisenberg's symbolic calculations into matrix mechanics. Dirac independently discovered the main ideas of the Born–Jordan paper through the transformation theory.[17] An important paper by Born, Heisenberg and Jordan gave a logically consistent exposition of matrix mechanics. These were the seminal papers on the subject.[18] For some years to come students wishing to learn these abstruse developments had to resort to reading these papers, unless they attended Dirac's or R H Fowler's lectures in Cambridge.

Another exciting line of research which also had its beginnings with Rutherford at Manchester was that of 'artificial transmutation of elements'. On arriving at the Cavendish Laboratory, Rutherford, with the help of James Chadwick and research students, continued what were called 'disintegration experiments'.[19] Until 1923 the Cavendish had the lead in this field. Rutherford told the British Association at Liverpool that they were living in the heroic age of physics. Later, competition and even controversy came from laboratories in Paris, Berlin and Vienna.[20] Searches for different and more energetic projectiles and improved detectors would keep many research workers busy. These led to the building of the Cockcroft–Walton accelerator, the automatic (later counter-controlled) cloud chamber and electronic counters. Each contributed towards important discoveries, Nobel prizes and the instigation of fresh fields of research in physics.

Speculations as to the structure of the nucleus abounded from the early days of its inception.[21] Thus Andrade was prompted to say in his book, *The Structure of the Atom*,'...the subject has offered a vast field for what the Germans call "Arithmetische Spielereien", which serve rather to entertain the players than to advance knowledge'. To account for the observed facts of transmutation, scattering experiments and radioactivity, the nucleus was assumed to be composed of hydrogen nuclei, alpha-particles and electrons.[22] Rutherford himself had a satellite model of the nucleus, which he mentions as late as 1930 in his book with Chadwick and Ellis, *Radioactive Substances and their Radiations*. Later Chadwick surmised 'So it came about that the main line of attack of the Cavendish was on problems connected, directly or indirectly, with the atomic nucleus. This was perhaps the first time that a great laboratory had concentrated so large a part of its effort on one particular problem.'[23]

In 1912 W Friedrich, P Knipping and Max von Laue had demonstrated the diffraction of x-rays by crystals. Following on the heels of this discovery the Braggs pioneered the field of x-ray crystallography—'in the truest sense scientists began to cast light on the structure of matter'.[24] W L Bragg established a strong school of crystallography at Manchester between 1919 and 1937, as Professor Lipson tells us in his contribution.

X-rays had always presented an ambiguity. The discovery of the Compton effect[25] in 1923 revived Einstein's corpuscular hypothesis of light. De Broglie's thesis (1924) of matter waves introduced wave–particle duality into physics. The physicist's dilemma was expressed by W H Bragg in the well-known aphorism that light behaves like waves on Mondays, Wednesdays and Fridays, like particles on Tuesdays, Thursdays and Saturdays, and like nothing at all on Sundays. De Broglie's ideas were developed by Schrödinger into wave mechanics by 1926. In the same year Schrödinger and Eckart independently demonstrated the equivalence of matrix and wave mechanics; two disparate approaches had given identical results! From now on progress was rapid. With Max Born's probability interpretation of the wave function

(1926), the uncertainty principle by Heisenberg (1927) and proof of electron diffraction (1927), a revolution in physics was achieved. The new quantum mechanics was applied to many new and old problems and its success was phenomenal.[26]

The theory of relativity, which bestrides the whole of physics, had already transformed physical thinking. Dirac, who had achieved an elegant synthesis of these two physical schemes in 1928 in his wave equation of the electron, recalled:[27]

> ...in the 1920s the whole idea of relativity ...was still quite young. It did not make a splash in the scientific world until after the end of the first world war and then it made a very big splash. Everyone was talking about relativity, not only the scientists, but the philosophers and the writers of columns in the newspapers. I do not think there has been any other occasion in the history of science when an idea has so much caught the public interest as relativity did in those early days, starting from the relaxation which occurred with the ending of a very serious war.

Had Goethe written Faust in the first quarter of this century, the question put to Faust 'How do you stand to religion?' may well have been replaced by 'How do you stand to relativity?'[28] Relativity had its sceptics and its adherents. There were many books in English on the subject and many lecturers in British universities were well versed in it. In contrast, books on the old quantum theory were few; in fact the catalogues did not have a rubric for this topic.[29] James Jeans' *Report on Radiation and the Quantum Theory* for the Physical Society (1914) remained a standard text in English for a decade.[30] Then came Sommerfeld's *Atomic Structure and Spectral Lines* as a godsend to undergraduates. The essays in this book are illuminating about the role of lecturers and textbooks in acquainting the students with these novel ideas in physics.

Towards the end of the 1920s, when physics seemed replete with the successes of quantum mechanics, new problems surfaced; these were mainly due to the ubiquitous electron. Conservation of energy could not be reconciled with the continuous β-ray spectrum—to save the situation Pauli postulated the neutrino in 1930. Many experimental results could not be reconciled with the inclusion of electrons in the nucleus. The negative energy states of the electron in Dirac's theory could not be explained satisfactorily.

Solutions came miraculously in 1932 with the discovery of the neutron by James Chadwick and the positron by Carl Anderson. That year also saw the artificial transmutation of lithium with the Cockcroft–Walton accelerator and the discovery of deuterium. The results of the work done with the cyclotron also became available. 'Nuclear physics' came of age. A heady period of activity in physics had begun; artificial radioactivity was discovered by the Joliot-Curies in 1934. On the theoretical front, the discovery of the neutron led to renewed thinking about nuclear structure and forces. Fermi used the neutrino hypothesis in his theory of β decay in 1934. Building on this Yukawa, in 1934, postulated a 'heavy quantum' to explain nuclear forces and radioactivity.[31]

Blackett and Occhialini's confirmation of the positron and of Dirac's hole theory, and their striking photographs of cosmic ray showers, gave unprecedented momentum to the study of cosmic rays. The total number of publications in this field, which had amounted to perhaps just over 600 up to this time, rose to 2900 by 1938. The field of study extended from terrestrial magnetism to astronomy to the subatomic world. Karl Darrow described the subject as '...unique in modern physics for the minuteness of the phenomena, the delicacy of the observations, the adventurous excursions of the observers, the subtlety of the analysis and the grandeur of the inferences'.[32] The energies available in cosmic rays were 10 000 times greater than those of any particles known before; it is not surprising that physicists were prepared to accept a revision of their cherished theories at such awesome energies.[33] The penetrating component of the cosmic rays was eventually identified as a new particle (now the muon) by Anderson and Neddermeyer in 1937; this was erroneously assumed to be Yukawa's particle for the next 10 years. The field of particle physics was waiting, poised for exploration.

A series of experiments with neutrons, by Fermi's group in Rome, the Joliot-Curies in Paris and Otto Hahn in Berlin, eventually led to nuclear fission on the eve of World War II.

It is within this framework of developments in physics that the students were acquiring the traditional skills of a physicist, picking up the latest developments in the subject, discovering their propensities and making choices about their research careers. They in turn carried the torch forward and many became the mentors of the next generation of physicists. We are fortunate to have the opportunity to learn from some of the architects and builders of the edifice of physics about the influences that shaped them.

Notes and References

1 From the late 1860s most Institutions had introduced laboratory classes. Sviedrys R 1976 *Hist. Stud. Phys. Sc.* 7 405–36.

2 In Germany the first chair of theoretical physics was held by Kirchhoff at Berlin in 1875. Theoretical physics was taught in Britain, but the chairs did not appear until the 1920s.

3   Forman P, Heilbron J L and Weart S 1975 Physics Circa 1900 *Hist. Stud. Phys. Sc.* **5** 33.

4   Davy's peroration in the Inaugural Discourse at the Royal Institution in 1802 was directed at his friends, the 'Lake Poets'. See Sharrock R 1962 *Notes & Records R. Soc.* **17** 57–76; Lankester E R 1917 *Science and Education* (London) (seven lectures at the Royal Institution in 1854 by Whewell, Faraday, Tyndall *et al* on 'Science and Education'); Sedgwick A 1832 *Discourse on the Studies of the Universities* (Sedgwick advocates science as a worthy subject for university study, and states that its free and unimpeded development could only be to the glory of God.)

5   See the bibliographies: Brock W H 1975 From Liebig to Nuffield: a bibliography of history of science education, 1839–1974 *Studies in science education* **2** 67–99; Roberts G K 1985 in *Recent Developments in the History of Chemistry* ed. C A Russell p 24–48 (London: R. Soc. Chem.). Cardwell D S L 1972 *The organisation of science in England* (London: Heinemann).

6   Lavoisier 1789 in *Traité Elémentaire de Chimie, Works I* in the classification of elements lists light and heat. Davy (1812 *Elements of Chemical Philosophy*) follows him in this.

7   See Curtis S J 1967 *History of Education in Great Britain* (London: University Tutorial Press) Ch. X. An important consequence in England of the Act was the provision of free places in all the fee-paying secondary schools for children from elementary schools. This was the beginning of the 'Scholarship Ladder to the University'. For Scotland see Curtis, Chapters XIV and XV.

8   In 1902 there were 300 teaching posts for scientists in British universities, 250 places in government laboratories and 180–230 posts in industry. In contrast, in Germany the chemical industry alone employed over 1500 scientists. See MacCleod R and MacCleod K 1976 The Social Relation of Science and Technology, 1914–1939 in *The Fontana Economic History of Europe* ed. C M Cipolla Part I p 306.

9   Chorley K 1950 *Manchester Made Them* (London: Faber and Faber) p 106.

10 Melville Sir Harry 1962 *The Department of Scientific and Industrial Research* (London: Allen and Unwin).

11 Chapman A W 1955 *The Story of a Modern University: A History of the University of Sheffield* (Oxford: Oxford University Press) p 299.

12 Oxford admitted women to full membership of the university in 1920. Cambridge only offered titular degrees with limitation on numbers in 1921, full membership came a quarter of a century later. Howarth T E B 1978 *Cambridge Between Two Wars* (London: Collins) p 35–42.

13 Robertson P 1979 *The Early Years: The Niels Bohr Institute 1921–30* (Copenhagen: Akademisk Forlag).

14 Beyerchen A D 1977 *Scientists under Hitler* (New Haven, CT: Yale University Press); Lord Beveridge 1959 *A Defence of Free Learning* (Oxford: Oxford University Press).

15 Heilbron J L and Wheaton B 1981 *Literature on the History of Physics in the 20th Century* (Berkeley, CA: University of California Press) p 330–3, for the interested, lists many sources.

16 Birks J B (ed.) 1963 *Rutherford at Manchester* (London: Heywood).

17 Dirac P 1926 *Proc. R. Soc.* A **109** 642–53. For Dirac's own account of the development of his ideas see Weiner C (ed.) 1977 *History of Twentieth Century Physics* (New York: Academic Press) p 109–46 (*Scuola Enrico Fermi, Corso* **57**).

18 Van der Waerden B L 1967 *Sources of Quantum Mechanics* (New York: Dover) reproduces these papers, with a brief historical sketch, as well as others that were germane to the development of matrix mechanics. Mehra J and Rechenberg H 1982 *Development of Quantum Mechanics* (Berlin: Springer) is a monumental work on the subject.

19 By 1924 they had demonstrated artificial transmutation of all elements between B and K except C and O (Chadwick J (ed.) 1965 *The Collected Papers of Lord Rutherford of Nelson* vol. 3 (London: Allen and Unwin) p 113). Blackett's cloud chamber photographs showed for the first time, in mid-1924, that the assumed disintegration of nitrogen by alpha-particles was initially an integration process (Blackett P M S 1925 *Proc. R. Soc* A **107** 349).

20 Disagreement, lasting from 1923 to 1927, arose over the results of transmutation experiments carried out by Gerhard Kirsch and Hans Pettersson at Stefan Meyer's Institut für Radiumforschung in Vienna. See Darrow K K 1931 Some Contemporary Advances in Physics—XXII Transmutation *Bell Sys. Tech. J.* **10** 628–55 for a brief account.

21 For these speculations see Kovarik A F and Mckeehan L W 1925 *Bull. Nat. Res. Counc.* **10** part 1, ch. 6.

22 Rutherford, in his Bakerian Lecture to the Royal Society in 1920, relates the state of knowledge and plans for future research in this field (Chadwick J (ed.) 1965 *The Collected papers of Lord Rutherford of Nelson* vol. 3 (London: Allen and Unwin) p 14–38). Nuclei such as 'X_3^{++}' were incorrectly identified as probable units of nuclear structure; the mistake was corrected in 1924 (Chadwick 1965, p 120) but in 1920 it played an important part in Rutherford's speculations about the existence of the neutron. Thus the search for this neutron was carried out at the Cavendish for many years. (See 1964 *Proc. 10th Int. Cong. Hist. Sci. (Paris) 1962* (Paris: Hermann.) Antonius van den Broek, a lawyer and amateur scientist

from Holland, seems to be the first one to have explicitly suggested the inclusion of electrons within the nucleus (van den Broek A 1913 *Nature* **92** 372–3).

23   Oliphant M 1972 *Rutherford: Recollections of the Cambridge Days* (Amsterdam: Elsevier) x.

24   Herman A 1973 Max von Laue in *Dictionary of Scientific Biography* vol. VIII (New York: Scribner).

25   Stuewer R H 1975 *The Compton Effect* (New York: Science History Publications).

26   Jammer M 1966 *The Conceptual Development of Quantum Mechanics* (New York: John Wiley). See also 1980 The Beginnings of Solid State Physics *Proc. R. Soc.* A **371** 1–177.

27   Dirac P 1971 *J Oppenheimer Memorial Prize acceptance speech* (New York: Gordon and Breach) p 46.

28   The speculation is not so irreverent; a physics 'Faust' was performed at the Copenhagen Institute. For a full text of the parody see Gamow G 1972 *Thirty Years that Shook Physics* (London: Heinemann) p 165–214; see also Lady Jeffreys' reference to it in Chapter 3.

29   *A Catalogue of British Scientific and Technical Books* (British Science Guild) gives the following information.

Number of books in various subjects for three different years

		Year	
Subject	1921	1925	1930
Physics	269	318	424
Relativity	14	32	39
Quantum topics (under Spectra and Molecular Physics)	1	3	14 †

†Many of these 14 were translations from German or bound collections of lectures.

The textbook situation started to improve in the 1930s; American books appeared. Kevles D J 1978 *The Physicists* (New York: Knopf) p 214 and Crowther J G 1970 *Fifty Years with Science* (London) p 39.

30   Dissemination of the old quantum theory is discussed in Kuhn T S 1978 *Black Body Theory and the Quantum Discontinuity, 1894–1912* Ch. IX (Oxford: Clarendon).

31   Brink D M 1965 *Nuclear Forces* (Oxford: Pergamon); Brown L M

1981 Yukawa's Prediction of the Meson *Centaurus* **25** 71–132. The Yukawa particle (the pion) was discovered in cosmic rays in 1947.

32 Darrow K K 1932 Contemporary Advances in Physics—XXIII *Bell Sys. Tech. J.* **11** 148–84.

33 Many physicists, including Bohr, Blackett, Oppenheimer and Bethe and Heitler themselves, believed for some time after 1934 that the Bethe–Heitler theory and hence QED breaks down at high energies. In this atmosphere Shankland's erroneous experiment (1936 *Phys. Rev.* **49** 8), which revived the ghost of the Bohr–Kramers–Slater theory (1924 *Phil. Mag.* **47** 785), added to the doubts and provoked from Dirac a note in *Nature* (1936 *Nature* **137** 298). See the chapters by Sir Bernard Lovell and Professor Burcham.

CHAPTER ONE

REMINISCENCES

R W Ditchburn

My reminiscences of my undergraduate course are limited by two considerations. Firstly, I entered Liverpool University in 1919 and time has eroded detailed memory. Secondly, I never took a university first year course. There were then, as now, two school examinations. The first one was roughly equivalent to O-level (ordinary level examination, taken at the age of 16) but it was accepted, when passed in certain subjects, by universities as a qualification for entrance and was generally known as 'matric'. I passed this at the age of 14 but stayed at school for 2 more years to take the Higher School Certificate which was, if anything, a little beyond A-level (advanced level examination, taken at the age of 18). Students who entered university with this qualification were excused the first year and expected to take two years over the Pass degree (in two subjects), followed by one year on the Honours degree (in one subject). My schooling had been so good (my father was Head and taught maths so I had extra home tuition if I had any difficulties) that I found the university Pass degree course very easy. This was partly because, in mathematics at least, the lectures were extremely good. I had coordinate geometry from a lecturer called Street whose lectures were a model of lucidity. Calculus was taught by Professor F S Carey. He was a little more difficult to follow but somehow inspiring. He was very short-tempered. It was said that he suffered a lot of pain from gout. One day he evidently thought that I was not listening to him. He said sarcastically 'Now Mr Ditchburn, you know all about it. Come and finish this problem.' I took the chalk from him and had no difficulty in finishing the problem, though it was my first experience as a lecturer. The next time he got cross with me was when I told him that I had elected to specialise in physics rather than in maths! Applied mathematics was taught by Professor Proudman. I think the lectures were competent but not so inspiring. Also, they did not go far enough to cover the maths needed in the physics course which was to follow.

I do not remember the physics lecture course of my first year (the university second year). I think the lectures were competent but did not greatly arouse my interest. The practical course was interesting. To get through the two year course in one year I had to do two experiments in one session instead of one. That I could do so was due to the fact that the class was well organised—all the apparatus for an experiment was set out and all in working order. Perhaps there was too little in the way of a problem element. It was all so straightforward. I had one amusing brush with Professor Wilberforce who took the class. One of the experiments was to measure g by Kater's pendulum. Times of oscillation about two knife edges are measured and g is calculated from a formula with a main term proportional to $T_1{}^2 + T_2{}^2$ and a correction proportional to $T_1{}^2 - T_2{}^2$. By a little ingenuity I set the knife edges so that T_1 was almost equal to T_2 and brought Wilberforce the result calculated only from the principal term. He said I should have included the correction and I pointed out that it was obviously negligible. He said 'Oh no. I want you to learn about the correction. Go and do it again.' So I had to upset my accurate adjustment and give him a new set of results. I think one of the objectives of a practical course should be to reinforce associated theory, though I think the Kater correction was of small value if a student, in a few minutes, could adjust the pendulum so that the correction was negligible.

After I got the Pass degree examination I went on to work for the Cambridge Scholarship Examination in physics and maths and also for the Honours degree in physics. My father got me a book by Radford containing problems much more difficult than those I had done at university. With this book and his help I improved my mathematics. When I went for the Cambridge Scholarship my competitors were schoolboys and I had more than a year of university behind me. This helped me to gain a major scholarship at Trinity.

The Honours physics course at Liverpool in 1920–22 was not well taught. Professor Wilberforce, as far as I remember, did not give any of the lectures. The only lecture of his which I remember was a brilliant one to a 'popular' audience. He was very popular among the students and well known as a fell walker of the Lake District. There is a plaque to his memory in one valley. It was a pity that he left the final-year teaching to others.

There were four of us in the final year. Most of our lectures were given by J Rice (who wrote a book on statistical mechanics—a good book in its time). He was nearly always late for a lecture—up to an hour late. The four of us used to loiter in the hall chatting while awaiting him. The chief laboratory attendant said he would put up a notice 'Stand— for four asses.' Rice got behind with his lectures and at the end of term he lectured all morning. He gave us three solid hours of the mathematical theory of electromagnetism. He then did the same in the afternoon and all of the following day. We were just scribbling down what he wrote on the blackboard and hoping to understand it later. We would have done better to read a book.

I think the staff in mathematics was in every way (except in numbers) as good as a good university staff of today. In physics, though Wilberforce and Rice were both men of high ability, I do not think the course lectures were good. The practical courses were better.

Figure 1.1   The George Holt Physics Laboratory, opened by Lord Kelvin on 12 November 1904. (Courtesy of Liverpool University.)

The main fault of the Liverpool system was that, as far as I remember, there were no tests during the course, no tutorials and no check on whether students were really understanding their lectures or their reading. I was a very quick thinker and could read a book rapidly and—as I thought—grasp the ideas. But sometimes I had not understood deeply enough and had only a superficial grasp of the ideas. Someone to discuss with me and to ask me searching questions would have been invaluable. Also, when I had two years to do the Honours degree in physics, I had time on my hands and got bored. I ought to have been advised to take a considerable number of lectures in maths (especially applied maths but including some pure maths). There was no tutor to consider my course as a whole and advise me. I think that in this respect things are better now than they were then but that there is still room for further improvement.

Figure 1.2 Lyon Jones Professor of Physics from 1900 to 1935. A student's impression. (Courtesy of Liverpool University.)

After my degree at Liverpool I went to Trinity College, Cambridge. As I was still only 19 I could not go on to research immediately but was excused Part 1 of the Tripos, essentially the first two years of the course. I had an early success in getting a Senior Scholarship at Trinity, partly because most of my competitors had only a few months of University work behind them.

Here I found a brilliant staff. It was the golden age of the Cavendish (intellectually, not in regard to money). Lectures were given with enthusiasm. They stimulated, even if some of them had faults in lecturing technique. Also, I gained a great deal from my supervisor C D Ellis (later Sir Charles Ellis FRS). He talked to me about the latest discoveries. I remember how once he explained the newly discovered Compton effect. Later, he told me of a paper which criticised Compton's work and threw doubt on his theory. After another month he came back to the subject with 'Compton has rallied his forces ...'—a suitable phrase from an ex-army officer. A little while ago I had for review a book which stated that a theory by Duane did not become widely known and was discarded unheard. In my review I was able to say that I remember a detailed discussion with Ellis in which its pros and cons were set out.

Research students were employed to do tutorials with students and I did this. I think that if someone with experience had given me two or three hours advice on taking tutorials it would have helped me to give more to the students. However, I must have been regarded as successful because I was made a 'sub-lector', which was a recognition that I was on the College academic staff, albeit at the lowest level.

Practical courses in Cambridge were very good. I think they owed a good deal to Thirkill (afterwards Master of Clare College). I never took the earlier part of the practical course under G F C Searle, who was one of the pioneers of practical physics teaching. He was a man under considerable psychological tension and often raged at student mistakes. A friend of mine acted as an assistant to him and one day Searle bawled out for him to come. When he got there Searle said he had been called because, being a young and inexperienced demonstrator, he would not believe without actually seeing that anybody could make such a foolish mistake as this man here (pointing with his finger) had just done. It was said that few men and no women got through his class without tears! I think some of the women were tougher than that!

Nevertheless, Searle was basically a kindly man. I got to know him and I went for walks with him. When I was not in good health he was most sincerely anxious for me to try faith healing and I had to be very tactful.

Searle criticised the tutorials given by the younger generation. He said that when a student came with a difficult question about classical physics the young tutor would brush it aside and then proceed to give a tutorial on his own research interests. This never happened to me with C D Ellis and I hope it never happened to any of my tutorial students, but I think Searle had a point. It did happen sometimes. Does it still happen now?

I think that two students were taken together at tutorials and have often wondered what is the best number. I think it is four or five. With that number a skilful tutor can lead a discussion and see that they all take part. They can be made to interact to their mutual benefit, though it is not easy for the tutor if one in the group is very bright and another very dull. With more than five students one is almost sure to be left out of the discussion.

A Senior Fellow in Dublin once asked 'Do you give your research students the subject on which to work?.' When I said 'Yes' he replied 'That is the hardest part, you should collect all the PhDs.' Well, in the Cambridge of my day the supervisor set the problem and really wasn't expected to do much else. A distinguished biologist is said to have invited his pupil to breakfast to discuss the subject of his research. The professor talked brilliantly throughout the meal on everything except biology. When the student sensed that the professor was about to say goodbye, he stammered out 'What about my research problem?' The professor pointed to the shell of the egg he had just eaten and said 'Find out why that egg is brown.' The student took the hint, did a first class research on the processes of coloration in animals and in due course became a very distinguished biologist himself.

Rutherford had a number of problems auxiliary to his main researches and, I suppose, gave them to students whom he considered of less than average research ability without explaining in what way their results would be important. Consequently, they were inadequately motivated. I remember sitting in the rooms of one who said to me gloomily 'There are some researches that are as much use as counting the number of blades of grass on the lawn out there.' It did not occur to him that a biologist counting the number of grains of corn and hence estimating the fraction of seed which germinated might find out something important.

Also, in setting a problem, inadequate consideration was given to the availability of apparatus. It was assumed that a good student could make any apparatus he required—from 'pink string and sealing wax'. I remember one American who had less respect for the authorities than we had. He advised one man to go to J J Thomson and say 'Give me a noo [new] pump or else a noo problem.' I told my friend that if he did the reply would be 'You had better go to a noo lab.' Do supervisors nowadays always consider the availability of apparatus in choosing problems? I think most of them do give this some consideration but not always quite enough.

My research supervisor was J J Thomson. He had a theory of photons as closed tubes of electromagnetic force and this predicted a kind of general absorption (in gases) proportional, I think, to the wavelength. I looked for this in mercury vapour but without any hope of finding it because I didn't believe the theory was correct. At the end of the year I had convinced J J that I was only finding unresolved Hg_2 bands etc and we mutually agreed that I must do something else.

Quantum mechanics suggested that certain experiments on resonance radiation could yield results of theoretical importance. With JJ's agreement I set up apparatus. Then a paper arrived from Göttingen giving the results of the experiments I had proposed to do. I thought it was no use going on and then proposed to JJ that I should take up absorption again, but in potassium where quantum theory predicted absorption associated with photo-ionisation. I got no help in technique from JJ but he did give me very wise advice on at least two critical points. The methods of photographic photometry were then new and he asked what accuracy I thought I had achieved in the measurement of plates. When I told him he said I should remeasure a plate and see how well the results agreed. The measurement of a plate with the crude methods then available was laborious and lengthy but I did as he said. When it was done and I was able to show him the two sets of measurements agreeing within the accuracy I had claimed I felt it had been worthwhile. I gained something in confidence as regards the work. At another time I had been doing experiments on absorption for some time and got into a rut. He said to me 'You are not going to get more out of this kind of experiment. You must think of something else.' Note that he shook me out of the rut but he told me to think again. He didn't do the thinking for me. I did then think of a new line of attack.

Though I did not get technical advice from JJ, I got it elsewhere. H W B Skinner, a senior research student at the time, came one day and sat down to talk with me about my experiment. At first he was most discouraging. I felt he was telling me that the experiment was no good and anyway I couldn't do it. Then he seemed to say (not in so many words) 'Well if you are determined to go on and not commit suicide, I should do ...'. Then followed excellent technical advice. I realised that it was worth listening to his 'moan' to get his advice.

Once I was in difficulty over a Gaede rotary pump which had seized up. Together with a friend or two I was trying unsuccessfully to free it. The pump included a porcelain portion and breakage of that would have been very serious (as regards the state of laboratory finances). F W Aston happened to pass. He made a simple suggestion which solved the problem. I think the younger research students could get technical advice both from older students and from the staff, but some were too diffident to seek it.

One aspect of the lack of supervision was that there was no check on a research student overworking himself. J R Oppenheimer thought that mind and body were non-commutating or at least non-interacting entities. He did theoretical physics all evening (and probably far into the night) and practical physics in the day time (on the bench next to myself). One day while we were talking he suddenly collapsed and I caught him to save him from falling. It has been suggested to me that since I prevented him from cracking his skull on the floor I am responsible for the Atomic Bomb. I don't feel any guilt that way, though I suppose it is true that without Oppenheimer the bomb might have been six months later and the Japanese might have surrendered before it was ready. The world would never have heard of Hiroshima!

I did attend some lectures on mathematical physics as a research student but what I did was left almost entirely to me and I did not do enough. I also improved my knowledge in several 'unofficial' ways. I felt greatly honoured by being invited to join the Kapitza Club, which met weekly and discussed a paper which was 'hot news'. Sometimes the lecturer was a distinguished stranger (Heisenberg gave an account of the uncertainty principle when it was very new indeed). More commonly a member of the club took an hour to expound a recently published paper (often a German paper). When my turn came the key paper by Hund on molecular spectra was suggested. I demurred that it really needed a better mathematician and R H Fowler offered to help me out. I got stuck about two-thirds of the way through the paper but couldn't get an appointment with Fowler. When at last I got one and called at his house he was in his bath and, unlike Archimedes, didn't do physics in the bath! When I got to the meeting I gave the paper up to the point where I had stuck and then said I couldn't understand the next paragraph. The paragraph was read out and, even though Dirac was there, it was debated for an hour without a firm conclusion. About a fortnight later at the Cavendish Colloquium a research student (I think it was A H Wilson, later Sir Alan Wilson and President of The Institute of Physics) expounded the paper completely.

In addition to the Kapitza Club and the Cavendish Colloquium I also attended less frequent meetings of a mathematical–physics club called $\nabla^2 V$ and of the Observatory Club. I met Eddington at both of these and greatly admired him. From these four sources I was kept up to date with advances in physics outside the field of my own research.

At Liverpool there were some lectures on relativity and, though I don't remember them well, there must have been lectures on radioactivity because I considered the possibility (I suppose when I was not sure of Cambridge) of writing an MSc thesis on γ-rays. Quantum mechanics did not exist when I was at Liverpool and I do not remember the Bohr atom being taught there, though it may have been. At Cambridge the whole place was humming with discussions about the latest news concerning advances in physics. It was like waiting for the latest news from the battle fronts.

I think the main difference between teaching in the early 1920s and now is that the practical side of physics has been down-graded. Lecture demonstrations have been replaced by slides and overhead projection. Less importance is given to practical classes and to practical ability in the examination. Too much weight is given in the examination to the ability to reproduce strings of equations from the textbooks. On the other hand, project work has been introduced. I think it is very hard to maintain a high standard of project teaching. When projects are introduced into a department lots of good projects are suggested by members of staff. These last for two or three years. Then comes a times when staff members are racking their brains to find new projects. It is a bit easier when you have cooperative projects involving four or five students, but then it is very difficult to ensure that all students are really pulling their weight. With these multi-student projects there should be frequent planning meetings at which a member of staff should be present as an observer. He should interfere only if there is a proposal that would endanger either students or apparatus. Occasionally he might say a word to bring a diffident student into the discussion.

CHAPTER TWO

REMINISCENCES OF SHEFFIELD AND CAMBRIDGE

T E Allibone

I was fortunate to go to college in 1921 when many soldiers from the ranks and officers up to the rank of Captain were in their second or third year in the university, so we had colleagues around us far more mature than has been customary since those days, with the exception of the years after World War II when students did their National Service before entering college. I, for one, would like to see a return of National Service for all boys, especially those about to continue studies in a university. I recall the earnestness with which these older men attended lectures and did their laboratory experiments with great enthusiasm and determination to master the tricks of the exercise. I recall that the other influence these older men had was in sport; they substantially ran the football, tennis, swimming and shooting teams so the younger folk had rather a thin time.

It is not possible for me to make comparisons of my experiences in those far-off days with modern times; I have never been associated with university teaching, having spent my whole working life in industry, and in retirement I merely hold two research Professorships so I am not in contact with students at undergraduate level.

I was taking an Honours physics degree, which in those days meant that if you had credits or distinctions in three Higher School Certificate subjects you were excused Intermediate BSc, and in my first year I took Pass degree mathematics and Pass degree physics, thus leaving two years for the Honours course. We had what I would assess to have been some excellent lecturers. The Prof, S R Milner FRS, was a very quiet-spoken man but gave splendid lectures, particularly to the advanced students though at times too advanced for the beginners. He always lectured to the first year so that he got to know his pupils well. His strong suit was mathematics and he put us through Maxwell's equations smoothly though I am ashamed to say I cannot use them today. This reminds me of a remark made to me by Mark Oliphant some years ago when he gave an immediate reply to a difficult problem; I asked him how he could recall Maxwell so easily, he told me that as he lectured on this every year he could always think out a problem fundamentally on those lines. I wish I could. In retirement Milner wrote several Royal Society papers on the electron wave equation and Eddington's E-numbers and I had the honour of being asked to write his Memoir for the Royal Society.

Milner had spent the war years x-raying soldiers at the General Hospital so this probably made him less absent-minded and more business-like than he would have been, for he was otherwise a typical absent-minded professor; a lovable man with a charming wife.

Dr R W Lawson had been a prisoner-of-war for four years in Austria but he was allowed to do scientific research on radioactivity there and had translated Einstein's Relativity; these two subjects were his speciality. Dr Curtis, also back from the war, dealt with general physics but we only had him for one year as he left for a Readership at King's College, London, followed by the Professorship at Armstrong College, Newcastle. Mr J R Clarke, a wartime Captain almost killed in Flanders, had been the first physicist in the Metropolitan–Vickers Electrical Company research laboratory before being appointed to Sheffield; he had translated le duc de Broglie's book on x-rays, and specialised in atomic structure; a very good lecturer. There were a few others specialising in parts of physics as part-time maths/physics staff. My recollections are that we had a mixture of presentations, some lecturers giving us cyclostyled notes, Dr Lawson did these well and his 50-minute lecture would consist of amplifying these, answering some questions and preparing us for the next lecture notes thus giving us ample time to study the set books as the subject unfolded. All spoke up well and tolerated no noise, but as I said, the ex-Service men were there to catch up the years they had lost and brooked no nonsense.

Laboratory equipment was somewhat restricted with the large classes and we had to work in pairs; four afternoons a week 2 PM till 5 PM, Wednesday being sports day. Almost every experiment could be done in one afternoon, just a few stretched over two. The lecturers went round the labs questioning, helping where necessary, and marking all our lab books, thus we were taught to write up our work well; this could not have been a universal practice in later years, for many of my own staff in a research laboratory did not keep good lab books and had to be instructed in the art. We had glass-blowing lessons from a very good lab steward and I became quite proficient; this stood me in very good stead later in life as I will recount.

We had terminal exams at Christmas and Easter; I have found many students later in life who have had none or, maybe, one or two such terminals compared with our six or seven in three years. Now as I see it, exams involve certain techniques which can probably only be mastered with practice. What I am saying has little to do with the candidate's knowledge or ability; it concerns merely the approach to an exam paper, to composing answers in a given time and in an orderly manner, and this can be learnt with practice. It can certainly be improved with practice for it demands a strict discipline. I am a firm believer in a strict personal discipline; indeed as I have worked for many years with very high voltages a strict discipline of thought and action is the only way of avoiding electrocution.

We were expected to know sufficient French and German to be able to struggle through a scientific paper and in the final Honours exam we had to answer one question set in each language. The question was in the form of a quotation out of, let us say, de Broglie's book or from Poincaré and one from Planck or Einstein; we had to be able to understand those and then comment in English. As I had Matric in both languages I did not find much difficulty, but with Britain's entry into Europe I would recommend that all students in science should be obliged to have a working knowledge of two languages, and further I would recommend all lecturers should encourage their pupils to travel overseas in the two main vacations, preferably on foot and alone and thus have to fend for themselves in the country just to keep fed.

In our final year the Prof asked each Honours student to study a small piece of contemporary physics and then give two or three one-hour talks on this at the Saturday morning colloquium. I was given the conflicting views expressed by C D Ellis and Miss Meitner of Germany on the relation between the energy of β-rays and the γ-rays from the same element at disintegration, so I had to read about eight papers and then compose my thoughts; my friend doing the same course had to deal with Lord Rayleigh's work on the light of the sky, so the Prof's idea meant that we were brought right up to date on matters of immediate interest. This is of course much easier today with the advent of television science programmes, but at that time, apart from, say, *Nature*, current scientific topics were never discussed in the press. It gave me a great thrill when I met Ellis and Miss Meitner in the flesh within the next year or so.

Another event in our final year was the Departmental evening soirée; each of us had to stage an experiment of his choice and in addition to members of the university the soirée was open to senior schoolchildren and people in industry in Sheffield. I chose to set up the 'singing arc', a DC carbon arc into the circuit of which I injected audio-frequency currents from an amplified microphone; the arc gave out a loud sound of moderately high quality music. I must have exposed myself to too much ultraviolet for I had a very severe erythema for a week. My friend showed 'active nitrogen', another of Lord Rayleigh's discoveries.

A few trips were organised by our Physical Society. As a schoolboy I had been into about six of the great works in Sheffield. I had seen the

12 inch deck armour being rolled in John Brown's Works for the battle-ship *HMS Hood*, turbine shafts and railway wheel tyres being forged in Vickers, and silver ware and silver plating in Mappin and Webb's; now we went to see a cotton factory in Manchester, the soap works in Warrington, the railway works in Doncaster and we went to see Bragg's laboratory in Manchester and Whiddington's ultramicrometer in Leeds, so we covered a nice mixture of pure and applied science in our outings. This mixture was manifest in another way too; the Professors of Physics and also of Chemistry were automatically members of the Faculty Boards of Engineering and of Metallurgy so were kept close to the activities in the applied sciences which were of paramount interest in Sheffield's industries. I and, later, Charles Sykes were both beneficiaries of this close connection. I might, in this context, just jump ahead a few years: in the Applied Science Department of the University, that is the engineering, metallurgy and glass technology faculties, all housed in a part of the university a mile from the Arts and Pure Science and Medical Departments, there had been set up an Applied Science Committee comprising the three or more professors, the pure science professors and some industrialists from Sheffield; all in good time I was the Chairman of this committee for a decade. We met twice a year and one of the professors would describe the work of his department and then we made a tour for an hour or so. We often heard of pieces of apparatus which the department would like to have and very frequently one of the representatives of industry would be able to offer some new or some unwanted piece of apparatus which might go some way to meeting the need of the department. In this way industry was able to give direct help and at the same time be kept up to date with the work of the department and with the state of knowledge in that subject; it was a most profitable collaboration often leading to the placing of contracts with the university.

I had finished the Honours physics set experiments by the end of the second year and the Prof suggested that in my third year I might do a bit of original research work. Sheffield had been famous under the preceding professor of physics, the late Professor Hicks FRS, for spectroscopy and the optics lab was well-equipped. Milner suggested that I should investigate the infrared spectrum of hydrogen, a subject on which no work had been done. So I learned the optics of gratings, had to make a lot of apparatus in glass, a pump, McLeod gauge etc and learned to cut glass photographic plates, panchromatic, in complete darkness with a diamond cutter and then to sensitise these plates with infrared dye. The work was finished by Easter and I wrote up the thesis for my final exam and later my paper was sent to the Royal Society for publication; a wonderful boost for any young man beginning research. I am deeply grateful to the Prof for the encouragement he gave me. The department as a whole was not strong in research. Lawson was slow, Clarke very occupied with the huge classes, especially the medical group taking physics in Part 1 of MB, ChB, and there were only two students taking MSc doing research. The DSIR had only been founded in 1916 and grants for research, amounting to £120 per annum, were few and far between so any small contribution such as mine helped to boost the standing of the faculty at that time.

I can recall some colleagues of those days; some of the ex-Service men went into teaching as also did the few women graduates in the pure sciences. One student, my close friend, went into administrative education and became, in due course, the Director of Education in Belfast. Several from pure science moved into applied science, engineering or metallurgy; Charles Sykes, following me, went to metallurgy and via Metropolitan–Vickers became the Managing Director of the great steel company Thomas Firth and John Brown. Another, gifted in languages, became the head of the Berlitz School of Languages. You will remember the old song 'I danced with the girl who danced with the Prince of Wales'; well I danced with a girl who became world famous—Amy Johnson who flew solo to Australia!

My generation from school did a little better in the final exams than the ex-Service men on the whole; I suppose they had got rusty in background knowledge during the two to four years of war, whereas we were able to recapture quickly all our physics, chemistry and maths encountered at school. But I always regarded it a great privilege to have studied with those fine fellows who had endured the mud of Flanders, the heat and flies of Mesopotamia or who had crossed the desert and entered Jerusalem with Allenby.

It was through Mr Clarke's continuing connection with the Metropolitan–Vickers Company that I was invited, at his suggestion, to spend two weeks in the Christmas vacation in Trafford Park at the research department and it was there that I first met C R Burch, with whom I had many contacts through a long life and was finally honoured to be asked to write the Royal Society Biographical Memoir of his life. In March I was offered a position in the research department provided I got a First in the finals, and the salary was twice the DSIR grant for which the Prof had made an application for me. So all in good time I entered an industrial career which lasted 50 years, mainly through accidents of history. During the summer I went to M–V (Metropolitan-Vickers) in Manchester to learn what I was to do after the holidays. The idea was to work on the preparation of pure hafnium, collaborating with Professor G von Hevesy who had first discovered and isolated that element; I was to begin with zirconium and its alloys and then move on to hafnium. The work was to be done under the guidance of Professor Desch FRS in the Metallurgy Department of Sheffield University and under von Hevesy who was at that time in Copenhagen. I was allowed to register for a PhD degree and spend some of the time in the M–V laboratory, the rest of the two years in Sheffield.

By September the first I had found digs in Stretford and began in Trafford Park working with the chemist who prepared pure zirconium tetrafluoride and I reduced this with aluminium in a high-temperature furnace, and with the metal so produced I was to start to make sundry alloys. And here it was that my glass-blowing stood me in good stead as I said before; we needed a McLeod vacuum gauge but the glass-blower was a difficult cuss and created all sorts of difficulties and excuses so I wildly said I would make one. This I did next day and it created such a stir that even the research director came to see the fellow who had done it. In due course I made a 7 kW vacuum induction furnace with which I could heat refractory metals up to 2000 °C and this I then took to Sheffield.

The Metallurgy Department was very famous as you would expect it to be in Sheffield, but its fame rested on ferrous metallurgy and no one was working on non-ferrous metals at that time. The PhD period was for me a period of learning some physical metallurgy as applied to the high-melting-point refractory elements and alloys. Prof Desch was a man of encyclopaedic knowledge and could give enormous help when quoting new original work, but he was not a man of any experimental aptitude so did not anticipate problems or troubles, nor did he ever suggest the way I should go. He came round at least once a week to follow progress and taught me to use the high-power metallurgical microscope just bought for the new lab and also taught me phase-diagrams. There were three other students in the lab and a new member of staff and the output of research was quite reasonable for a small university department. Prof G von Hevesy took great interest in my work but his interest was only in the final results, he was not concerned with my experimental difficulties and problems and I only saw him a few times. I had almost no contact with the undergraduates so can offer no comments; there were of course no ex-Service men by now. Sheffield was just picking itself up from a minor depression (created by the Washington Disarmament Conference which cut back on the building of naval vessels) so the courses were well attended and graduates all found jobs. Incidentally, students all went up to the pure science departments for their first year physics and chemistry but I was the only physicist in the Metallurgy Department and for company I kept in close touch with my old colleagues and, in fact, remained the secretary of the Physical Society. The ICI company had recently been formed out of Brunner Mond and other chemical companies and the Research Director, Major Freeth, elected a Fellow of the Royal Society that very year, was touring universities offering research grants to graduates to enable them to stay on in college for the PhD degree, as I was doing. The salary he was offering was extremely generous; some of the recipients already had their PhD and were employed as permanent members of staff to work for a time in the university but, it seemed to me, they were not well supervised and some did not work hard. Within a very few years ICI had to cut back expenditure and most of these men were left high and dry. The M–V Company never went to town to that same extent and weathered the storm of the Great Depression better than did the ICI research workers.

It was during the Michaelmas term of my second year that Dr C D Ellis came from the Cavendish Laboratory to lecture to our Physical Society on the disintegration work of Rutherford and Chadwick using α-particles to change some of the lighter elements. I had always wanted to go to Cambridge so at dinner—to which I was kindly invited by Professor Milner—I asked Ellis if there were any scholarships available to non-Cambridge graduates for research; he told me of the Trinity and Caius scholarships but warned me that first I must suggest some line of research to Rutherford and gain his acceptance to enter the Cavendish Lab. Now just at that time Dr Coolidge of the General Electric company of America had constructed a Coolidge x-ray tube but fitted with a Lenard window to allow the electrons to emerge and this was from a 300 kV tube. So I suggested to the Research Director of M–V that I might ask Rutherford if he would support a programme of research using a half-million volt electron beam of considerable current, say, a milliamp, to look for nuclear disintegration by electrons. The Director at once said he would help me with apparatus if Rutherford agreed. So I wrote a programme of research, sent it to Cambridge, was interviewed by the old man who agreed to accept me if I could be self-financing. I applied to Caius College and by July was awarded the Wollaston Research Studentship supplemented by a DSIR award.

The zirconium work went well and by September I had written my PhD thesis and had my viva the day before I left for Cambridge in October. The M–V Company wanted the work to continue so I recommended my friend Charles Sykes to succeed me; he was a year behind me in the Physics Department, had taken his degree and with a DSIR grant had begun some work suggested by Prof Milner. The Prof very generously let Sykes leave his work and continue in the metallurgical faculty, registering for a PhD there instead of in physics; I say 'generously' because Milner had had so few research students to add lustre to his department and he knew that Sykes would have been a jewel in his crown; instead Sykes did excellent work for two years in the Metallurgy Department before going to the M–V Company and doing work there for which he was awarded the Fellowship of the Royal Society. In due course, 10 members of the Research Department of the M – V Company were elected to the Royal Society, surely a record which ought to figure in the Guinness Book of Records.

You will note that Sykes and I had gained our PhDs in metallurgy within a two-year period; I do not know whether the regulations would allow this today, but I can truthfully say that in both years I had only 3 weeks holiday in the summer and 3 more in all at Xmas and Easter, whereas in Cambridge the holiday would total at least 12 weeks in the year. In my case I had a lot of apparatus to make, Sykes only added a little and he was able to devote all the time to the alloy work; neither of us had any distraction and we gave no tutorial sessions to others and our emoluments were such that we did not need to work to earn supplementary income.

In Cambridge I never encountered undergraduates except medical students whom I tutored for their physics exams in Part 1 of the MB degree. My whole time was spent doing research and in those days we really did live on a shoe-string, the sealing wax/string era lasted till I had left. I was fortunate in having help from the M – V Company; my friend Brian Goodlet, in charge of the High-voltage Laboratory, designed the 600 kV Tesla transformer, the only kind of generator which I could have got into the room Rutherford gave me, the highest room in the Cavendish. I assembled this generator, after making all the supplementary parts not supplied from Manchester, and I made all the glass apparatus including a glass lathe. I went to Manchester to roll the thin aluminium and nickel windows needed to let the electrons out of the vacuum tube, and I made the deflecting solenoids and scattering chambers. In retrospect I realise that the task was too big to be undertaken alone in those days; Rutherford tried to support me with a junior assistant but alas he suffered from tuberculosis and had to leave me in three months; he was followed later by a Canadian but in three months he had to return to Canada.

I had several digressions, Prof Stratton roped me into the Cambridge eclipse expedition and the M – V Company sent me to Germany to meet Prof Rogowski and Dennis Gabor, the experts in cathode-ray oscillography, which was just then becoming extremely important, but Rutherford gave me strong support. He was an excellent supervisor of young research workers: he would congratulate you or let you see he was disappointed with your work; you knew exactly where you were, whereas his deputy, Dr Chadwick, would listen to your account, say nothing and then leave you so that you had no idea whether what you had reported pleased him or not. I have tried all my life to react as Rutherford had done whereas Cockcroft, having lived under the same tutelage, emulated Chadwick, saying nothing, or 'yes' when he meant 'perhaps' or 'perhaps' when he meant 'no'. Rutherford would come round the lab about once a week or so, sit wherever there was a chair or upturned box, light his pipe and listen. He demanded good simple English in the written word; I recall when he told me to apply for a Senior 1851 Exhibition Award I wrote in a hurry as time was short and used technical jargon; he was very annoyed and I learned my lesson and hope I have taught many of my staff the same lesson.

I doubt whether work for a degree has changed very much; I have examined many PhD theses, particularly of students working on the big particle accelerators and on high-voltage generators, and all have had a lot of construction work to do; of course I mean students engaged on experimental work, not the theoreticians. The most important consideration for good work by beginners is good supervision. I have encountered a case where the lecturer set two students a project which would take about six to eight weeks to complete, he probably specified exactly what should be done but he never went near them for five weeks and then it was found that they had set up the apparatus wrongly so the time had all been wasted; a simple glance by the lecturer at the apparatus would have shown him their initial error and it could have been corrected at once. This example is not the first I have met; we had it in Cambridge and doubtless it's still there. The great Cockcroft/Walton experiment of 1932 is an example of the opposite; Rutherford was watching the two week by week struggling to get the apparatus to work. Incidentally theirs was a good example of the need at times for two to work in harness, neither could have done the experiment alone, it was just too difficult. But they kept going off at a tangent and could not see the way ahead, only Rutherford saw the true goal and he literally pushed them into it by constant badgering.

The research school in physics at Cambridge was by far the largest in the country; there were over 30 research students studying for the PhD degree when I was there. It was a course of a minimum of three years and was always begun by an apprenticeship in 'Chadwick's Attic'. This was primarily designed to teach all research students how to handle radioactive sources, and very necessary it was too, for there had been accidents with sources and two members of staff had lost fingers from exposure to strong activity. But in addition we learned to make gold-leaf electroscopes, to count scintillations on zinc sulphide screens caused by alpha-particle bombardment and the glass-blower gave us a simple course in his art. So it was the Lent Term before we began the research project set for us, usually, but not always, serving as a junior worker under a more experienced man. In addition to Rutherford, Chadwick and Ellis, there were several senior scientists who supervised in various subjects. Thus Prof C T R Wilson, the Jacksonian Professor, supervised Wormell, Schonland who came over from South Africa for a year, and, I think, Jack Ratcliffe at first, in atmospheric electricity; there was Prof

G I Taylor holding a Royal Society Professorship, doing work on the borderline between mechanical engineering and physics, a charming man who always gave friendly help to all who asked; Aston was perfecting a new mass spectrograph with Bainbridge as an assistant for a short time and there was Rutherford's son-in-law, Fowler, who supervised a large group of theoretical scientists of whom you will doubtless hear from others. Rutherford, Aston, Taylor and Fowler played golf, 18 holes, every Sunday morning on the Gogs.

Then there was the Russian, Kapitza, who had just completed the installation of his alternator, which on short-circuit could produce a magnetic field of 300 000 Gauss; Cockcroft designed the coils to support the huge forces created by the large current from the machine interacting with the magnetic field, but he also virtually ran the business side of the magnetic laboratory, the largest venture Rutherford had ever sanctioned in the Cavendish, and, as well as this, Cockcroft was completing some molecular ion research for his PhD. Kapitza was an extremely able electrical engineer as well as being a mental giant and an extrovert, a law unto himself, but he could be put in his place at times, such as when he went to the Senate house incorrectly dressed and was refused entry by the Proctor. The Canadian W B Webster was one of his research students, a wealthy man who had crossed the Sahara from Kano to Algeria alone, the first to have done this by car. Kapitza was there till 1934, when he was deprived of his passport by Stalin as he was about to return to Cambridge from his customary summer visit to the Soviet Union. There was Blackett with a demonstratorship, developing the cloud chamber for automatic recording of ion tracks. He supervised many students as the years passed by and managed with a very small budget; indeed, he was very critical of the generous finance accorded to Kapitza and, I suspect, was very glad when he got the Chair at Birkbeck. He was moderately 'red', very enamoured of the Soviet Union and we used to go to his house on Sundays to see films depicting the wonders of the Communist regime. Cockcroft and I had been to Russia and had seen other sides of the coin; we were never so enamoured. Bernal, a very kind man but very scruffy, ran the mineralogical research work but Rutherford was so opposed to his outstanding Communism that there was no love lost there; Wooster was one of Bernal's pupils but very few studied this branch of physics.

Behind this galaxy of younger men stood 'JJ', who came daily into the Cavendish to do research and to supervise several students such as the two Taylors, one of whom later became the Managing Director of Imperial Metals Company. I remember encountering JJ as he entered the porch with a grin wider than usual; I asked the cause of his mirth but before I could frame my question he told me his explosive news; he had just seen the great hurdler, Lord Burleigh, get round Trinity

Great Court, hurdling over the corners, whilst the clock struck twelve, a feat never previously achieved.

Almost all of the younger men left as soon as they had got their degrees; Skinner to Bristol, Ditchburn to Trinity College, Dublin, Dymond to Edinburgh, Schonland to Cape Town, D C Rose from Canada to the NRC at Ottawa, E J Williams and H Braddick to Manchester. E Watson, H Cave, G C Lawrence, Ben Lewis and other Canadians went back home. From the Antipodes, Mark Oliphant, after a short period as Demonstrator took the Chair at Birmingham and Leslie Martin and others returned to Australia and New Zealand. We had only two women students, if I recall correctly, Miss McKenzie who married my colleague Harper in due course, and Miss Salaman from overseas. Several scientists came from Europe for short visits, Wertenstein from Poland, Chariton from Joffe's laboratory in Leningrad, and a few others drawn to the genius of Rutherford. I almost forgot E T S Walton who came from Trinity College, Dublin, in my first year and worked in the same room as Cockcroft and I, trying to accelerate electrons, at first, by changing the strength of a magnetic field in which they pursued spiral orbits, the very beginning of a betatron. Then he tried to accelerate ions by the process we now call the linear accelerator; both these experiments failed and he was about to try something else when the new theory of Gamow appeared; this suggested that there might be a penetration through the barrier surrounding a nucleus instead of a bombarding particle having to surmount that energy barrier. It was Cockcroft who first read the manuscript of this paper in January 1927 and at once wrote the famous project suggesting to Rutherford that hydrogen nuclei of 300 kV might penetrate a beryllium nucleus and create disintegration; with a current of a milliamp there might be sufficient disintegrations to be detected with moderate ease. Thus, with Walton's great help, atomic disintegration was put on the map.

Well I have finished. In a way I wanted to stay on in Cambridge but the Great Depression was raging and I was offered the directorship of the finest high-voltage laboratory in Europe. I did put in for a Caius Fellowship in the last few weeks in Cambridge. There was only one Fellowship and there were two candidates; I do not know even to this day whether, had I been successful, I should have stayed on for 3 years, and then perhaps for life, I was not successful; the other fellow got it. Now let me see, who was he? Oh yes, I remember, he was a chap called Nevill Mott.

CHAPTER THREE

A CAMBRIDGE RESEARCH STUDENT IN THE 1920s

Bertha Swirles Jeffreys

In 1925, at the age of 22, I became a research student in the Faculty of Mathematics at Cambridge. It had been fortunate that Northampton, which had been slow to carry out the implications of the 1902 Education Act, did in fact found a good Secondary School for Girls in 1915 and I went to it on its first day with a scholarship won from an Elementary School of which my aunt was headmistress and at which my mother taught. I had no lack of home encouragement. My father had died in 1905 and we lived in an extended family. I learned quite as much from my self-educated grandfather and from another aunt as from the professionally trained teachers. There was no scientific background, though I am sure that with better opportunities that would have been my mother's inclination. She subscribed to the *Scientific American* for me and I wish that I had kept the copies.

The atmosphere of the Northampton School for Girls was forward-looking and stimulating. I was taught mathematics by three Cambridge women, two of them wranglers. (I have been taken up on this because in those days Cambridge had not admitted women to full membership, but they had taken exactly the same examination as the men, so let it pass.) I had 4 happy years in the sixth form as I passed the Oxford Senior Local Examination (roughly the equivalent of O-level) when I was 14. My main subjects were mathematics, physics, chemistry and botany, but I kept up French and Latin, the latter till I had gained exemption from the Cambridge little-go (preliminary examination) and I started German; this has stood me in good stead in later years. Mathematics became my main interest. It would have been good for me to have more competition. The Boys' Grammar School was some distance away. We lost a good mathematical teacher to them in the war. The borrowing of their apparatus to determine the mechanical equivalent of heat was an annual event and, more important, we were invited to hear Sir J J Thomson when he came to their Speech Day. I liked learning languages and was furious when a boy who was learning Russian told me it was not a suitable language for a girl. I was no longer a girl when I did begin to learn it in 1957 and managed to translate E P Fedorov's *Nutation and Forced Motion of the Earth's Pole*.

Undergraduate Years 1921–4

I won a Scholarship to Girton and read for both Parts of the Mathematical Tripos. Miss Cave-Browne-Cave kept up the old system of coaches, which was dying out in the men's Colleges. In 1921 she had engaged four 'pure young men', Ingham, Pars, Burkill and Francis. She did send us to lectures by Stratton on optics and hydrostatics in our first term; these are not exciting subjects at that level and I had no idea then of Stratton's distinction as an astrophysicist. We studied Jeans' *Electricity and Magnetism* with Mary Taylor (later Mrs E C Slow). She was an important influence and encouraged me to become a physicist. She was working with Appleton and in 1924 she went to Göttingen where she was awarded a PhD in 1926 for a thesis on the propagation of electromagnetic waves from a horizontal dipole over the Earth.

The Tripos as I read for it was not a preparation for the revolution in physics that happened in 1925. Somehow I dodged learning much geometry and algebra and that might have been useful. I attended Cunningham's lectures on electricity and magnetism and acquired a considerable facility with problems in classical dynamics and hydrodynamics. My optional subjects in Schedule B were 'theory of functions' and 'elliptic functions'. I am not clear why I was advised to choose them and I was not enthralled. However, in June 1924 I was in the list of wranglers and 'satisfied the examiners in Schedule B'. I had not taken enough optional subjects for 'Distinction'.

I returned to Girton in the Long Vacation to prepare for a change to physics. I had been out of practice in experiments for three years and I went to G F C Searle's Intermediate class in the Cavendish. He has a reputation for having been hard on women students, but I had been warned that one should 'stand up to him' and I must say that in his own brusque way he was kindness and helpfulness itself.

The experiments were carried out with prepared apparatus; we did not have to make our own out of sealing wax and string at this stage. I remember getting a very bad result for 'g' (with Kater's pendulum?)—a poor preparation for marriage to a geophysicist. There was a visitation to the Laboratory by Fellows of the Royal Society one afternoon and I demonstrated an experiment to C V Raman. During that Long Vacation I also struggled with black body radiation as expounded in Preston's

Heat. 1924 was the summer of the British Empire Exhibition at Wembley, which I visited several times; this sounds remote now.

Postgraduate Years 1924–5

In October I embarked on the course for physics in Part II of the Natural Sciences Tripos. My supervisor for theoretical work was C F Sharman of King's College. As it happened he was one of a number of men who had won Scholarships from Northampton Grammar School. I heard that he said to someone that I overloaded him with written work I had produced. (This reminds me that at school at the age of 14 I produced for a holiday competition a History of Architecture which was described by the adjudicator as a 'monument of industry' and I sometimes fear that this sums me up; my reward then was a bound volume of some of Chopin's pianoforte works which is still in use.) Sharman introduced me to a good little book on the quantum theory, as it then was, by Fritz Reiche. He drew my attention particularly to Einstein's *A*s and *B*s and the memory has been pleasing in learning the principles of the laser. He also impressed on me the importance of the experiment of Gerlach and Stern in 1921.

In the Part II Laboratory I was not very happy. Appleton had just gone to his Chair in London. He used to run the class with Thirkill, who was left in charge with A H Barton and J A Ratcliffe as assistants. Ratcliffe tried to teach me to make a T-piece and I was clumsy, largely I think owing to shyness; it is funny to realise now that Ratcliffe and I were of the same year, having pursued different courses. I was the only woman in the class and I think Thirkill may have been slightly afraid of me. Years later I came to appreciate him as a helpful Governor of Girton in the transition period before it became a College of the University. I had constant trouble with ammeters and found a friend in Tilly, the laboratory assistant. It seems to me now that I spent nearly all the Lent Term over a sort of electrometer and then passed on to the measurement of Young's modulus for glass by hanging weights over a plate and measuring interference fringes; I cannot now describe the result as after I had left it set up overnight I found that the weights had been too heavy and the glass had broken. On the whole the men left me to myself but on that occasion two of them were very sympathetic. The laboratory work was from 10 AM till 5 PM three days a week and we also attended lectures by Rutherford, J J Thomson, C T R Wilson and Thirkill. Towards the end of the Lent Term I suffered a minor disaster; in bicycling back the two miles to Girton one evening I skidded into a ditch and my precious practical notebooks fell out of my bicycle basket and were never the same again.

My recollection is that my imagination was caught by the Bohr theory of spectra when I read the account in *Atoms and Rays* by Sir Oliver Lodge (1924) in the Easter vacation. I was visiting a friend, Isabel Sayers at Duffield. Her father was an electrical engineer whose title in the LMS Railway was Telegraph Superintendent at Derby Station; he did pioneer work on signalling, triggered off, I believe, by the great blizzard of 1916. He was interested in modern developments in physics and had recently bought the book, which I found on his shelves. Later in that vacation at home I had a bad attack of influenza. I returned to Cambridge before I was really well and for the Easter Term suffered from what was diagnosed as sub-acute rheumatism; I fear it may also have been that I was not getting on very well. The Girton Director of Studies, Miss M B Thomas, was on leave and Miss Elles of Newnham was my adviser. Many years later in visiting Geology Departments in various parts of the world we were greeted by 'How's Gertie Elles?'.

Here I must pay a tribute to Bertha Philpotts (later Dame Bertha Newall) who from 1922 to 1925 was Mistress of Girton. An Icelandic scholar, she enjoyed holding the office of 'Head of the Department of Other Languages' in the University. She emphasised the importance of research and, although I was not going to take the physics examination, she encouraged me to apply for a College research studentship; the College had a very generous benefaction for research from Sir Alfred Yarrow, the shipbuilder. With Thirkill's help I also applied for a DSIR grant. I was sent to see Rutherford who said, 'They tell me you are not much good at experiment; you had better go and see Fowler.' I think I did not know then that R H Fowler was married to Rutherford's daughter Eileen. He added, 'My daughter's friend Cecilia Payne seems to be getting on quite well in astrophysics'—not extravagant praise considering the success of her Harvard PhD thesis on Stellar Atmospheres. From her recently published autobiography (1984) I gather that her experiences in the Cavendish were much like mine. I should have been glad of support from her and from Mary Taylor at that stage. Cecilia left Cambridge for Harvard in 1923 and I did not meet her until 1950.

Dr Searle believed strongly in faith healing and during that 1925 summer he tried to convince me but, like Cecilia before me, I remained aloof from it. By doctor's advice I had my tonsils removed in June—a then fashionable remedy—and returned to Cambridge for the Long Vacation Residence. I had my Yarrow Studentship and in July I heard that I had been awarded a DSIR grant. This made £200 a year plus anything I could earn by supervision—the Cambridge term for what everyone else calls tutorials. It is pleasant to recall that one of my pupils was Dr H D Megaw.

For my application to be a research student registered for a PhD I had to supply a title for my research. Fowler wrote, practically on the back of an envelope, something about following up some new ideas of Heisenberg's; I kept the bit of paper for a long time but it has now disappeared. It seems that Heisenberg visited Cambridge in that summer but I did not know this until I read Dirac's account of that time. At Fowler's suggestion I went to see D R Hartree who lent me his notes of Fowler's lectures and chapters of his own thesis. He and his wife became lifelong friends.

I read Andrade's *Structure of the Atom* and studied Born's *Vorlesungen über Atommechanik* and Sommerfeld's *Atombau und Spektrallinien* in German. These I bought in paperback and had them bound, not expensive in those days. During August I had my first taste of travel abroad, a holiday with my mother in Switzerland, which included the train journey to the Jungfraujoch.

Research Student 1925–8

In October I returned to Cambridge as a research student, still resident in Girton. I worked in my rooms or in the Cavendish Library or in the Philosophical Society's Library where the librarian, Mr Matthews, was always helpful. Hartree suggested that I should work on the polarisabilities of some atomic cores by the series electron using a formula of Born and Heisenberg. I went to see him and Fowler two or three times a term when I wanted help. There was no regular appointment. I might have thought that Fowler was not taking much notice of what I was doing but in the Easter Vacation of 1926, when I was at home, he wrote to say that A Unsöld was doing something very similar to my work. I rushed over to Cambridge for the day to read his paper. There is a reference to it in the paper in the *Proceedings of the Cambridge Philosophical Society* that I completed in the Easter Term and read at a meeting of the Society in July; I was persuaded to read it by Dr Searle who appeared to be in charge of that meeting though he was not an Officer of the Society. I seem to remember that Oppenheimer backed out of reading his paper at the meeting. It happened later that my husband was President of the Royal Astronomical Society when the Gold Medal was awarded to Unsöld.

I made abstracts of a lot of papers (there was no Xerox then!) and in the winter terms of 1925–6 I went to lectures by Fowler on statistical mechanics—effectively part of his book—and on quantum theory of spectra and to Cunningham's lectures on electron theory. In the Easter Term Cunningham lectured on the structure of solids and the dynamics of crystal lattices (Born's book) and Fowler continued on quantum theory. On the same mornings as Fowler, Dirac gave his first lectures and Fowler and all his class went to them. Dirac's title had been announced in the winter as 'Quantum Theory of Specific Heats' but when he gave the lectures it was 'Quantum Theory (Recent Developments)' and they were on his own work and Heisenberg's. We were privileged to be present at what would now be called a breakthrough. The lectures were given in his characteristic style and, as I have said elsewhere, when I read anything he has written I hear him saying it and others agree with me. Fowler was almost reading the papers overnight and pouring them out the next morning. It was not always easy to follow but he had the great gift of communicating his enthusiasm. The General Strike (or more correctly the Strike of the Triple Alliance) took place during that term, but the lectures continued through it. I rather think Hartree must have been driving a train because he had a tremendous interest in and knowledge of railways.

During that year Schrödinger's papers came out. I did not know that one could write for offprints so I bought the four numbers of the *Annalen der Physik* and had the papers bound, a volume I treasure. I remember a morning when a reference to the 1924 de Broglie paper sent me excitedly pedalling to the Library. In the early part of 1927 I read a paper on this at an evening joint meeting in St John's College of the Adams Society and the Girton Mathematical Society, the latter incidentally the much older of the two. This was a return match for a joint meeting at Girton in the previous year at which Cunningham lectured on 'Mathematics and Morals'.

Later in the summer at home I worked out the constants in the Rydberg–Ritz formula according to wave mechanics; when I returned to Cambridge Fowler approved of this but then, to my chagrin, I found that the work had already been published by Ivar Waller. I met him later when he visited Hartree and he remembered me when my husband received an honorary degree at Uppsala in 1977.

I became interested in the theory of the photoelectric effect, developed by Oppenheimer following Dirac's theory of arbitrary perturbations, and when I heard a talk by Ellis on the ejection of electrons from the outer atom during the emission of γ-rays I saw that this was a similar problem. Fowler said 'Put a Hertzian dipole at the centre' and I worked on this and published two papers in the *Proceedings of the Royal Society*, but unfortunately did not treat the problem relativistically, as was appropriate for radium; this was done a few years later by Hulme, and Mott and Taylor. There has been later work but I have turned to other topics, except that I was stimulated, about 1950, to study the classification of multipole radiation.

During the period from 1924 to 1927 there were visitors from abroad to the Cavendish. I remember particularly Langmuir, Franck and Sommerfeld. Also, there was Katherine Blodgett, whom I had met at lectures; she had been a pupil of Langmuir and was attached to Newnham College. As was customary she lived in the house of a senior member, in her case Mrs Bushe-Fox, widow of my husband's former tutor. She was, I think, the first American I knew at all well and she was very good fun; she entertained us with the story that Mrs Bushe-Fox thought the Heaviside layer was a sort of hen. In 1951 I met her again at the GE Laboratory in Schenectady where she was doing pioneer work on non-reflecting glass. Franck spoke of 'gayses' and 'wapours', but then few of us could have given a good lecture in German. Sommerfeld I think talked about the Goudsmit and Uhlenbeck paper on the spinning electron. The visits of these German physicists are of interest because at that time the newly formed International Research Council was keeping Germans out. A G Cock has given an account of this in *Notes and Records* (1983).

There was then no meeting place for theoretical physicists other than the small Cavendish Library. My work overlapped with that of Gaunt but we were both shy and reticent. It will surprise no one to be told that Mott was different from the others in that he was friendly and ready for discussion. Once when I asked Dirac about something I had done he pointed out kindly but firmly where it was wrong, but he is well-known to have been generally uncommunicative. Fowler did not have an office in the Cavendish until after I had left Cambridge. The societies that met in the evenings, the $\nabla^2 V$ and Kapitza Clubs, were not open to me as a woman. I ought to have pushed more, but it might have been counter-productive.

The year 1926–7 was my last as a research student resident in Cambridge. Three years were needed for a PhD and one could be spent elsewhere. Mary Taylor urged me to go to Göttingen and Fowler advised me to go to Max Born. It was time for me to get away from the shelter of Girton. My DSIR grant was for two years only. Girton elected me Hertha Ayrton Fellow but this was not enough to live on; I borrowed from my mother and aunt and paid it back over several years. This was no great burden but it gives me an antipathy to government student loans.

During the Easter Term of 1926 Maria Göppert (later Maria Göppert-Mayer, a Nobel Prize-winner) came to Girton, an arrangement made by Mary Taylor. After her return to Göttingen her father, a university professor, died and her mother kept on her large house by letting rooms and it was arranged that I should live there. I had said airily to my family that I could live in a garret and they were highly amused when I sent them a postcard of the house, Hoher Weg 7, where I arrived in September 1927, well advised on travel by Harwich-Hook by Mary Taylor. She arranged for me to join a *Mittagstisch* other than her own;

I had a regular midday meal there and picnicked in my room for other meals.

At his first lecture Born asked for volunteers for some jobs and I chose card-indexing his offprints; this I did in his beautiful library containing much music as well as scientific works. There was a spin-off as I kept the duplicates. Max Stobbe, who later came to Bristol, also helped. Language was a bit of a difficulty at first, but I think I seemed more fluent than I really was. I exchanged reading with a Frau Gelpke; she wanted *The Forsyte Saga* but I cannot remember what I read. Frau Göppert lent me various books and I enjoyed Sigrid Undset's *Kristin Lavransdatter* in German translation.

There were many lectures and meetings. Wigner and van der Waerden were developing the Group Theory approach and I found this difficult. Van der Waerden had a way of saying that a result was '*sehr befriedigend*'. Courant was heard to say that these quantum theory people read nothing but their own papers. Courant and Hilbert, *Methoden der Mathematischen Physik*, was of course required reading for anyone using Schrödinger's approach. I little knew when I had read it that I should be press-ganged into a dancing class because Courant wanted to learn to dance; some of the others were Levy, Neugebauer, Rellich and van der Waerden, the last two later brothers-in-law.

I had read Wentzel's work on the photoelectric effect and asked Born if I should go to see him in Leipzig as I was going to Dresden for Christmas to the family of Herr Wehlte, a schoolmaster who took English paying guests to improve their German. I stayed a couple of nights in Leipzig and was able to make an appointment with Wentzel. There was, I suspect, mutual surprise as he turned out to be a young man of about my own age, just off to Paris for Christmas. It was bitterly cold but I visited the *Gemäldegalerie* and saw the Thomas Kirche and the *Fölkerschlachtdenkmal*. I thoroughly enjoyed my stay with the Wehltes; as they spoke little English my colloquial German improved. It is sad now to think of that beautiful Christmas tree and the tables with presents for all the family and one for me. Later on correspondence ceased because it was clear that Herr Wehlte approved of the Hitler regime and I do not know what became of them in the bombing. They looked after my artistic education and I remember particularly a performance of *Die Meistersinger* under Fritz Busch, the Don Cossacks choir, the Sistine Madonna and van Eyck's triptych.

On my return to Göttingen lectures had not started. I had made a correction in the wave equation I used in my first paper on internal conversion; when I wrote to Fowler about this he told me in his reply that Dirac had made an exciting advance and this was the relativistic equation. I continued my work and also prepared applications for research fellowships and for an assistant lectureship at Manchester, for which Fowler gave me good encouragement to apply. On 1 March I had a summons to an interview there. This meant leaving Göttingen early and I was grateful to Frau Göppert for excusing me for short notice. I was succeeded by Maria's future husband and my predecessor had been H P Robertson.

However hard up I have been, I have somehow been able to afford concerts. I suppose I paid about three marks for tickets in Göttingen, where they were very good. For example I heard Adolf Busch and Rudolf Serkin early in their collaboration and I rejoice that Serkin is still playing. Orchestral concerts were in the rather ugly *Stadtpark* and I have a mental picture of van der Waerden with Emmy Noether in the gallery. When she died in the USA he wrote an obituary notice in the *Mathematische Annalen*, a brave thing to do in 1935. Everyone at the *Mittagstisch* seemed very knowledgeable about music. The only German physicist there was Hertha Sponer who later married Franck. There was a biologist, Fräulein Ilse, and during the war, probably in December 1940, I chanced on her outside Cambridge Police Station. She was a 'friendly alien' and had to register there. We recognised each other and I was glad to give her a welcome to our home.

I left Göttingen in March knowing that I was to return to Cambridge for the Easter Term to finish my thesis. I think that ten of us were interviewed for the three posts at Manchester. They were offered to Gertrude Stanley, Sydney Goldstein and me. She was a few years older than I as she had had school teaching experience before working with Hardy in Oxford. Goldstein came to a full lectureship a year later. Milne was head of the department but I had only one term with him as he went to Oxford. When I mentioned Milne to Born he said, in a surprised way, '*Aber er ist Astronom*' and it is true that he had been Assistant Director of the Solar Physics Observatory until 1924. Born was asthmatic and during the winter had often been away from Göttingen in the Alps. I understood this better years later when I had attacks myself and found the difference that a few thousand feet make.

I submitted my thesis, 'On some applications of the theory of perturbations in Quantum Mechanics', in the Easter Term 1928; on this I was given very little advice except to go and look at those of Dirac and Hartree, one thin and the other thick as regards bulk of paper, but both very meaty. The examiners were Darwin and Fowler and the *viva voce* took place with some formality in a lecture room in the Arts School. (They were both very large men and I relish a story told to me by Delbrück of a charade at Copenhagen; one of them as p leapfrogged over the other as q and then q jumped back over p, whereupon a board shot up bearing the legend $h/2\pi i$.) The usual channels were rather slow but Darwin was at a meeting in Cambridge later in the summer and he told me that all was well. I went off to a holiday in Bavaria and the Mathematical Congress in Bologna, which has an interesting history not relevant here.

When I went to Manchester in October 1928 the Hartrees and Mott went to Bohr's Institute in Copenhagen. Mott wrote to me that there was an interesting Russian called Gamow who had a theory of the penetration of a potential barrier by α-particles. Later Fowler asked me to revise Gamow's English in the 1931 edition of his book *Atomic Nuclei and Radioactivity*. Any theory to do with β-particles was under suspicion at that time and Gamow had a symbol, a sort of skull and crossbones consisting of α- and β-particles, to indicate this where β-particles were discussed. This was beyond the powers of the Oxford Press and it appears as $\sim$. I did my best and passed the script to E J Williams who removed some more of the 'residual Gamow'.

It was not until much later that I realised that Gamow's treatment of the connexion formulae at the boundaries of the barrier was unsatisfactory although the physical idea was right. This is a story against myself. In 1926 I had read the papers of Brillouin and Wentzel which eventually became the WKB method. Also, Harold Jeffreys had given me offprints of his 1924 papers in the *Proceedings of the London Mathematical Society*, but they lay in a drawer. I did not properly connect the two until I was lecturing at the Cavendish and he was producing his more elegant treatment of the approximation, involving Airy functions and published in the *Philosophical Magazine* in 1942. We had married in 1940 and I had learned that there were after all subjects in classical physics that were still of vital interest. He maintains that the method, now known as JWKB with various permutations, goes back to Green and Liouville. I then tried to improve on Gamow's treatment. I forget who it was that said when asked a question 'I don't know anything about the subject; I haven't even lectured on it.'

When I was in Göttingen there was a meeting of the *Gauverein* of the *Deutsche Physikalische Gesellschaft*, the only occasion on which I met Pauli. This was the first time I met the word '*Gau*', later to have the bad connotation with Hitler's *Gauleiters*. Frau Göppert used to lend me her *Deutsche Allgemeine Zeitung* and I knew of the misery that the inflation had caused, in some ways worse than the war. There was complaint at the Versailles Treaty, but I had no idea of the horror that was to come in a few years. In the summer of 1933 I met someone at the Royal Astronomical Society who said 'They have dismissed everyone at Göttingen, beginning with Emmy Noether.' I think the 'someone' was my husband but he does not remember it. During that year nearly everyone I knew left Germany. When after two years spent at Bristol and Imperial College I returned to Manchester as a lecturer in 1933 the Physics Department had welcomed Bethe and Peierls.

Teaching

My personal experience of the teaching of theoretical physics is of that provided by university departments of mathematics. Hartree succeeded to Milne's Chair in 1929 and in the following years there were courses on classical mechanics and electromagnetism and I gave a short course on special theory of relativity. In 1929–30 Mott's book, *An Outline of Wave Mechanics* (1930), was given as a course of lectures for all who liked to attend in the physics department. In 1937 Hartree moved to a Chair of Theoretical Physics and he made duplicated sets of notes on electromagnetism and wave mechanics. These are handwritten and owing to the method of reproduction they have become very faint. My copy is deposited with his papers in the library of Christ's College, Cambridge.

When I was invited to return to Girton in 1938 it was suggested that in the following year I should take over the course on quantum theory that H M Taylor had been giving in the Cavendish. By October 1939 he was already in the army and I gave the course during the years of the war. The teaching for the Physics Departments of Bedford and Queen Mary Colleges, evacuated from London, was amalgamated with Cambridge, so that the class was large. My course was considered too mathematical at first, but I think we adapted to each other as time went on.

In the Cambridge Mathematical Faculty optional advanced courses on modern developments were given from the 1920s onwards, and presumably earlier but I refer to the topics I have been discussing. In the standard Part II of the Mathematical Tripos, courses on atomic physics were not given until the late 1950s. This was done more thoroughly in the 1960s, but I could not help resenting what I can only call the 'Triposization' of a subject which to me was still young and fresh. Wave mechanics can be split up into examination questions that can be answered by someone with little idea of the physical background. This is, I fear, also true of older topics. I have not been involved in teaching since 1969 but I see from this year's lecture list that there are lectures on special relativity in the first term of the first year and on quantum mechanics in the second and third years.

I am not now in a position to make an effective comparison with the life of a research student in physics today, but I hope I have given some idea of what it was like 60 years ago. It was indeed an exciting era.

Postscript

A remark dropped by Harold Jeffreys refers to a time *before* the first war. 'I wondered when I first heard of Quantum Theory. I took my Cambridge BA in 1913 and started research at once. I joined the Observatory Club and an early meeting, probably the first, was addressed by Jeans, who brought Nicholson as a guest. There was certainly something about atomic structure and I asked whether the theory accounted for valency and Jeans replied that it had not so far.' Very shortly before Bohr's fundamental paper of 1913 Nicholson had arrived at the quantisation of angular momentum, but had missed the frequency condition. In order to interpret the spectra of the gaseous nebulae and the solar corona, he postulated the existence of four atoms (protyles) having the simplest possible structure and Fowler (the spectroscopist A Fowler, not R H) referred wryly to these as the elements that Nicholson was clever at inventing. Sommerfeld has a footnote about Nicholson on page 106 of *Atombau und Spektrallinien* (Sommerfeld 1924).

References

Cock A G 1983 *Notes and Records* **37** 249–88
Lodge Sir Oliver 1924 *Atoms and Rays* (London: Benn)
Payne C 1984 *Autobiography* (Cambridge: Cambridge University Press)
Sommerfeld A 1924 *Atombau und Spektrallinien* (Berlin: Vieweg)

CHAPTER FOUR

RECOLLECTIONS OF PHYSICS AT TRINITY COLLEGE, UNIVERSITY OF DUBLIN, IN THE 1920s

E T S Walton

I was a pupil at the Methodist College, Belfast, from 1915 to 1922 where I was fortunate to have had excellent teachers in mathematics, chemistry and physics, which were the subjects of most interest to me. I was anxious to continue studies in these subjects at a university and so I inquired about possible financial aid. I found that each county in Northern Ireland offered one scholarship of £40, renewable for a further two or three years, which could be held at any Irish university along with a university scholarship. I was lucky to be awarded one and decided to hold it at Trinity College, Dublin, where I was awarded a sizarship giving an exemption from fees and a free dinner each evening. A few other awards brought the total cash up to about £80, which was almost enough to cover the total costs. The value of money then can be seen from the fact that a good three-piece suit could be bought for about £4 or £5.

I had to decide whether to compete for a sizarship in mathematics or science. On studying recent examination papers, it was apparent that the standard in mathematics was high while in science it appeared to be very low. So I thought that anyone with a smattering of science could get high marks and the examiners might have to separate the candidates by the neatness of their writing, which would not have suited me. So I opted for mathematics. This situation may have arisen because many of the smaller Irish schools found it difficult to provide good science teaching in both physics and chemistry. Often only one subject was taught and sometimes none. At a much later date I was told by a government inspector of schools that in some schools no science was taught because it was believed that it might be dangerous for the religious beliefs of the pupils!

The teaching staff in physics in Trinity College consisted of only three members and this was also the case in chemistry. Other science subjects such as botany and zoology had only two members of staff. With such staffing it would be impossible to provide after the first year a single-subject degree course, which would have to be broader and at a higher standard to justify the award of an Honours degree. At this time the standard for entrance to Trinity College was very low and so the first year covered mainly work which should have been done at the secondary school. Three further years were required for the award of an Honours degree.

In the first year of their course all science, premedical, and first year engineering students had to take a general course in physics. They attended three lectures and did two hours of practical work each week. About 100 students were involved in this course. Those intending to continue to study physics in the following year were required to do an additional two hours of practical work each week. They also had to take a course in mathematics consisting of four lectures per week. In the second year the course involved four hours of lectures and six hours of practical work per week. The third year course was similar but mathematics was no longer compulsory. In the fourth year there was a small increase in the number of lectures and the time spent on practical work became indefinite. Chemistry was no longer compulsory but at the final examination physicists had to take a paper and a practical examination in chemistry although they had been examined on the same course a year earlier. The chemists were treated similarly in physics. In both cases the subsidiary courses accounted for 30% of the final examination. This was a peculiar situation but it did result in a broader education in science although at a lower level than could be produced in a mainly one-subject course taught by a larger staff.

In addition to passing the prescribed examination in their chosen subjects each year all students had to pass a general examination nick-named 'little-go'. This was taken at the end of their second year. The prescribed subjects were English composition, one of six named languages, Latin, logic, arithmetic and algebra, geometry, trigonometry and mechanics. In addition to a $1\frac{1}{2}$ hour written examination in each subject there was an oral examination in each language, in logic, in geometry and in mechanics. Students doing Honours courses in mathematics and in science did not usually have much trouble in passing the examination but those studying languages often had great difficulties in understanding mechanics. The standard required for passing the examination was low and those who failed could try again at one or both of two supplemental examinations. The course in logic was supposed to teach how to argue logically but when, as a student, I read the prescribed book I came to the conclusion that only those who knew already how to argue logically could understand the book!

Looking at the course of lectures as a whole, I think that it can fairly be described as an up-to-date one for about the year 1910. Readers who are interested in the practical course will find details in the appendix at the end of this chapter. A very short account of the history of physics in the College and of the better known people concerned now follows.

There has been a long tradition of mathematics and physics in Trinity College. The first professorship in physics was founded in 1724 and the holder was given the title of 'Erasmus Smith's Professor of Natural and Experimental Philosophy'. The words 'physics' and 'physicist' did not come into general use until about the second half of the nineteenth century. This professorship was funded from money left by Erasmus Smith who was a rich London merchant and who had bought land in Ireland from Cromwell. A similarly named professorship of mathematics was founded in 1762. In 1774 a professorship of astronomy was founded and an observatory was built. The interests of these three professors must have had much in common. The most famous of all of them was Sir William Rowan Hamilton whose work in dynamics turned out to be so very important in modern quantum theory. His prediction of conical refraction of light in biaxial crystals was important in confirming the correctness of the wave theory of light. Erasmus Smith's Professor Humphrey Lloyd demonstrated experimentally the correctness of Hamilton's prediction. He is also noted for his experiment showing the interference of light using only a single mirror. These two men must have had close contacts with the third Earl of Rosse, who was Chancellor of Dublin University. At his castle adjacent to the small country town of Birr he constructed a large telescope using only local labour. For 70 years this was the largest telescope in the world. With it, he discovered the spiral structure of some nebulae.

Two other people whose work was of interest to physicists were George Francis Fitzgerald and John Joly. Fitzgerald was an Erasmus Smith's Professor from 1881 to 1901. He died at the early age of 50 and is best known for the Fitzgerald–Lorentz contraction, which was important in the development of the theory of relativity. John Joly was professor of geology from 1897 to 1934. His inventions included the steam calorimeter, a form of colour photography and an instrument for measuring the melting point of very small specimens. His most important work was on the influence of radioactivity on the thermal history of the earth and its use in getting information about the age of rocks. Using his knowledge of radioactivity he was able to explain the existence of pleochroic haloes in some forms of mica. The presence in the country of the people mentioned would be expected to have had a considerable influence on the teaching of physics.

Students of physics often do not realise that university physics laboratories are a comparatively new phenomenon. Very few universities in the world had a physical laboratory in the modern sense before 1860. So it was common for professors to carry out experiments in their own homes or in their private college room and at their own expense. Stokes used to bring some of his apparatus with him to show in lectures. Even in Cambridge there was no university physics laboratory until the opening of the Cavendish Laboratory in 1874. So it was not a disgrace for Trinity College, Dublin, to be without one at that time. It did allocate two rooms to physics in a fine building erected in 1857. These rooms were vacated in 1906 on the completion of a handsome and large building specially designed for physics. For many years a description of the building was printed in the University Calendar and the boast was made that 'the city current is laid on throughout the building'! That boast remained in Calendars for 40 years! As a student I lived in College rooms during the years 1922–7 and when studying in them I had to use an oil lamp provided by myself.

Figure 4.1   Trinity College, Dublin, the Physical Laboratory *c.* 1920.

There were three storeys in the new building and a rope-operated goods lift was available. On the top floor there was a good lecture theatre designed to seat 144 persons. It was well suited for the showing of demonstration experiments. A convenient door led to two rooms in which demonstration and other apparatus was stored. Wires and ropes could be lowered from the ceiling to the lecture bench. This was very convenient for some of the experiments. At one end of the building there was a room built without the inclusion of iron in its structure or in its heating system, so that experiments sensitive to magnetic fields could be carried out in it. There was a large general laboratory with space for about 35 students and with sufficient apparatus to allow all of them to do the same experiment at the same time if working in pairs. On the ground floor there was a workshop fitted with a few machine tools—a medium-sized lathe, a drill on a stand and a pair of grinding wheels. All of these were driven by flat belts from an overhead shaft. The lathe was the worse for having been lent for munition work during the 1914–18 war. There were very few hand-tools and the stock of materials was very poor. I remember, as a research student, asking for some insulating tape and I was told that the laboratory did not stock it. However, there was always the possibility of getting a job done in the nearby engineering workshop.

When the laboratory was built, the names of the various divisions of science were painted on the doors of some rooms. In my time as a student the names had little or no connection with what was done inside. The only heat apparatus in the 'heat' room was a Joly steam calorimeter. The 'light' room was used as a second lecture theatre. It was indeed a light room as it was at the top of the building and it had seven very large windows. It would have been very difficult to make it dark enough for quite a number of experiments in light.

As previously mentioned, the staffing of the physical laboratory was poor, as was the position in other subjects. When I was a student it consisted of a professor, two lecturers and a person whose official title was, I think, an 'attendant'. His name was Tom Flood. He had been recruited when a young boy and had never been given any proper training such as a modern technician would get. His work consisted mainly of setting out apparatus for practical classes and for demonstrations. He could do some rough jobs in the workshop and he was a reliable and obliging person. The professor was William E Thrift, who in 1893 had obtained high honours at his degree examinations in both mathematics and science. He was made a Fellow of the College in 1896 and on the death of Fitzgerald in 1901 he was appointed to the vacant professorship. He was a very able man and very good at administration and committees, especially when chairman. The result was that much of his time was given to non-academic matters both inside and outside the College. He resigned from his professorship on becoming a Senior Fellow of the College in 1929 and in 1937 he became Provost. I attended both of the two lecture courses which he gave throughout the year. One was for the first year class and the other was for final year students. The former was clearly given and well illustrated by demonstration experiments. He was no good at keeping order in a large class of students, many of whom did not see the relevance of physics to their future studies. He got his brother Harry to attend the lectures, ostensibly to keep the attendance roll and help with the demonstrations, but actually he appeared to be there to help with keeping order during the lecture by spotting the evil-doers! The other course which he gave consisted of two lectures per week given to fourth year students throughout the year. These were very good lectures. They dealt with alternating current theory, bridge circuits, motors, generators, transformers, Maxwell's equations and also the works of J J Thomson, Millikan and Townsend. The last-named person would have been well known to him, as Townsend was three years senior to him in the College. Both of them competed at the same time at the examinations which were then the method of selecting persons for appointment as Fellows of the College. After four attempts Townsend abandoned the contest and then went to Cambridge to do research under J J Thomson, and subsequently became Professor of Physics at Oxford. Thrift managed to become a Fellow of the College on his third attempt. Such multiple attempts were very common at that time. Willie Thrift did not look after any practical classes in my time and so I did not get to know him very well personally.

The second member of staff in my time was Willie Thrift's brother Harry, who became a Fellow in 1909. He played 18 times for Ireland in Rugby Football. He was a very fast runner and he used this ability to advantage in the position of wing three-quarter. His great main interest was in sports and he did much for their development both inside and outside the College. I fear that the result of this was that he had only a very minor interest in recent developments in physics. I have now only one clear recollection of his lectures on heat. I felt then that he spent far too much time on the details of old controversies about the diathermancy of various materials, especially as these details were given in the then commonly used textbook on heat written by Thomas Preston. Harry Thrift was a good 'tutor'. Every student in the College had to have a 'tutor' but this title had lost all of its original meaning. It came to mean someone who counselled students about courses and regulations and cleared up difficulties. Harry Thrift was my tutor and he was very helpful on one occasion when a difficulty arose about the timetable for an important examination.

The third member of the staff at that time was John Hewitt Jellett Poole, named after his grandfather Provost John Hewett Jellett. He had a degree in engineering as well as science. For some years he was a research assistant to the Professor of Geology, John Joly, who has already been mentioned. He made many measurements on the radioactivity and on the very feeble magnetic properties of rocks using apparatus which he himself had constructed. In my time, he was the only member of the staff active in research and I think that he had a much better knowledge of recent developments in physics than either of his colleagues. He was responsible for the very few pieces of new equipment which came into the department. They were a mercury diffusion pump and a Wilson cloud chamber. There was very little money for apparatus

in the 1920s. The income of the Physics Department was about £450
per annum, out of which the wages of the 'attendant' amounting to
£220 per annum, had to be paid. So it was a great novelty to see a new
piece of apparatus arrive. I was involved with the cloud chamber because
in the last term of my fourth year I was given the project of getting the
apparatus to work and to take photographs of the tracks of alpha-
particles. The apparatus was beautifully made but the design was very
bad in three respects. Despite this, I was able to get some photographs
showing reasonably sharp alpha-particle tracks.

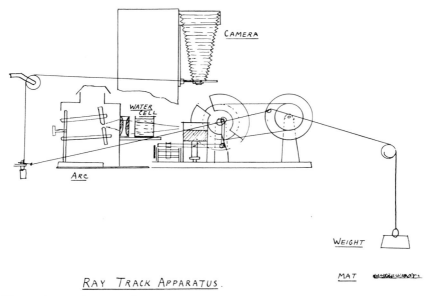

Figure 4.2   Diagram of the cloud chamber showing its working parts, drawn
by Professor Walton in his notebook in 1926. This Wilson–Shimizu type ray
track apparatus became available from the Cambridge Scientific Instrument
Company from 1921. (Courtesy of Professor Walton.)

   In my time as a student, no tutorial classes were provided in physics,
which may have been due to the smallness of the staff. Despite this and
the smallness of the numbers in many lectures, it was very unusual for
students to ask questions during a lecture, but sometimes a student
would ask a question after the end of the lecture. They could also seek
the answer by looking through various textbooks in the large College
Library. This library was very popular because it provided a quiet, warm
and comfortable place in which it was very easy to study up to 10 o'clock
at night.

Figure 4.3 A photograph of some alpha-ray tracks finally obtained.

As mentioned earlier, there was a long tradition of mathematics coupled with physics. Good students were encouraged to do as much of the Honours course in mathematics as they could manage. This was made possible because clashes were avoided in the timetables for the two subjects. A few students managed to get First Class Honours in both subjects.

Appendix 4A: Practical Courses in Physics

First Year (For students wishing to take physics in their second year)
Use of simple forms of measuring apparatus, densities, simple pendulum, coefficients of expansion, specific and latent heats, plotting magnetic fields, magnetic moments, tangent galvanometer, use of ammeters and voltmeters, electrical resistance, sonometer, wavelength of sound, measurements on mirrors and lenses.

Second Year
Surface tension, moduli of elasticity, hygrometry, mechanical equivalent of heat, Earth's magnetic field, uses of potentiometers, characteristics of dynamos and motors, chronograph, photometers, magnifying power of optical instruments, spectrometer.

Third Year

Cathetometer, Kater's pendulum, Joly steam calorimeter, Bunsen ice calorimeter, specific heats of gases, mechanical equivalent of heat, ballistic galvanometer, uses of potentiometers, quadrant electrometer, measurement of high and low resistances, thermal conductivity by Forbes method, use of fluxmeter, comparison of capacities, use of syren, Kundt's tube, diffraction grating, Fresnel's mirrors, Newton's rings, biprism, diffraction by a fine wire.

Fourth Year

Self and mutual inductances, capacity, $B-H$ curve, measurements on a dynamo, AC bridge circuits, coefficient of viscosity, focal lines of an inclined lens, polarised light, characteristic curves for a triode, generation of high frequency oscillations. Special project for each student in the last term.

CHAPTER FIVE

CAMBRIDGE 1923-6: UNDERGRADUATE MATHEMATICS

Sir William McCrea

This book is about physicists. Being called 'physicist' is an honour I should not presume to claim for myself. However, it was first thrust upon me when, as one who imagined he was a Cambridge mathematician, in 1928 I went to Göttingen to work for a year in Max Born's group. I discovered that in Germany (a) 'mathematician' meant one who did no physics, and (b) that Born and all his people were labelled 'physicists'. So I had no option but to allow them to call me what I should never have dreamt of calling myself at home. In the event, in Göttingen I avoided undue false pretence by spending most of my time doing what was regarded as astronomy. Ever since I have been called either mathematician or astronomer, never again physicist until being honoured by the invitation to write this contribution.

The value of the book must depend on it being a collection of personal experiences. Therefore a contributor is called upon to lay aside the cloak of impersonality which he is accustomed to wear in writing as a scientist; only when required to do this does he appreciate that this cloak is really a rather protective garment.

We are invited to recollect our days when we were undergraduates or research students between the wars—and to do so in regard to our learning to be 'physicists' within the meaning in the book's title.

One thing that this exercise brings home to me is the extraordinary sensitivity of one's career to details of timing. This is specially true in the early stages here considered. Had I been born only a few months earlier than I was, my career would have been advanced by a whole academic year: because of the war of 1914-18 my schooling would have been appreciably different; later on I should have had to start research on problems quite different from those upon which I actually embarked, and so on. In short, dates are crucial in the stories we have to tell. The reader should not be surprised if two of these stories are greatly different for no reason other than that their authors' birthdays are two or three months apart. Dates matter too in ways beside details of age. For example, Professor T G Cowling in an essay he calls 'Astronomer by accident' (1985 *Ann. Rev. Astron. Astrophys.* **23** 1–18) has recently told how as a schoolboy he hoped to go to Cambridge, but actually went to Oxford simply because in those days certain Oxford Colleges were out of line in holding scholarship examinations in March instead of December. So in due course it became natural for him to be E A Milne's first research student in Oxford—with eminently successful consequences.

Cambridge Undergraduates

My undergraduate years in Cambridge were 1923–6. In those times undergraduates coming up straight from school in the United Kingdom could be divided roughly into three sorts.

(1) Some came to do an Ordinary BA degree. In other universities there was something like this called a 'Pass' degree; regrettably, as I think, it seems to be a thing of the past. I believe there was some sort of examination in each term and a candidate had to accumulate a certain number of passes in (probably) three or four subjects 'studied' during his three years. One friend who was doing this assured me that, in the two weeks before each examination, he had to sacrifice some of his time in order to do some work for it. Most such men were worthy citizens possessing ample natural ability; they ran all sorts of clubs and societies, got blues, took part in dramatic performances, and kept the place going generally. Then and thereafter they were men of public spirit; out of their own resources they did all the things that are now supposed to be done on public money by 'students' claiming so-called 'sabbatical' years. In later life they followed callings in which specific academic training was not essential; they entered family concerns and/or took on public responsibilities, became games masters in schools and were in many ways the salt of the earth.

(2) Other students came up to read for a Tripos—elsewhere called an Honours degree—hoping to achieve a 'respectable' degree. These men would be somewhat disappointed with themselves if they finished with worse than a 'lower second', and somewhat surprised by themselves or their examiners if they did much better. They mostly aimed at careers in which an academic qualification was expected, the Church, schoolmastering, law (both branches), middle grades of the Civil Service (home and overseas), and other sorts of public service.

(3) The final group were those with avowed academic ambitions.

Most of these entered with a college scholarship or exhibition, which meant that most had been in a 'scholarship set' at school. So they had already done what humbler fellow undergraduates would take as first year university work. An undergraduate had to be in residence for three years in order to proceed to the BA degree. He had to do Part I of a Tripos before taking Part II of that, or some other Tripos. A few took Part II after two years, and then took a different Part II after three years, or maybe started research in their third year. For good or bad, the system meant that a man in this category had to decide two or three years before coming up what Tripos he would probably take. But the University, or the man's college, made no requirement that he should keep to that subject. My own brother, for instance, came up with an entrance scholarship in mathematics, but at the end of his first year he went over to medicine and did the Natural Sciences Tripos Part II in physiology.

At the time considered there were in Cambridge about 20 Colleges with an average of about 200 undergraduates each; a college would admit annually about 20 men in this category and would on average elect something like 3 new fellows. So even in this category most could not, and in fact did not, expect to go on to make a career in Cambridge. Some went into the Church, some into law, some into teaching in other universities—which were far less in number and all much smaller than now. Some went into schoolmastering, with aspirations to positions of high responsibility. A good many came up with the aim to enter the higher Home or Indian Civil Service. Only a minority wanted to 'do research'. Not to do this was regarded by nobody as a come-down. Nowadays almost every such student seems to think that he must stay on to do something called 'graduate work', or else rank as some sort of failure. In those days, in mathematics, physics and science generally, research meant as now the attempt to discover new knowledge. In other fields the corresponding object appeared to be to produce some scholarly work that, like the discoveries of some of the scientists, would lead to election into a college fellowship. This could lead to college offices that might become a man's main concern for the rest of his life. The majority of Fellows, I suppose, did go on writing and, of course, many attained high distinction.

Research was not, I would say, the obsession that it has become in more recent decades. Paradoxically, perhaps, in more ways than one this allowed higher quality research to get done. A more relaxed attitude allowed workers occasionally to pause for thought; there was not the same never-ending stream of refereeing and thesis examining; research students were fewer and those there were expected less attention and had to think for themselves.

Other undergraduates

A small percentage of undergraduates did not fall into the three categories I have described. In 1919 there had been a great intake of ex-servicemen, and a much smaller number in the next year or two. The majority of those were, I think, allowed to graduate after just two years. By 1923 there were few remaining as undergraduates.

There were also men coming up from schools overseas, mostly from various parts of the British Empire. It is well-known that some of these excelled in sports, notably in cricket.

Then there were some who had obtained first degrees in other British or overseas universities and who wished to add a Cambridge BA as well. Most of these were comparable in ability to the 'scholarship' category of normal undergraduates, and many went on to positions of distinction in public and academic life. In their own interests, some would, however, have been better advised to go straight into graduate work in Cambridge, rather than to prolong their lives as undergraduates alongside a majority two or three years younger than themselves.

It was a male world. There were the women's colleges, Girton and Newnham, discreetly away from the centre of Cambridge, but their undergraduates were not then full members of the University. At lectures they usually sat in isolation in front seats; they took care never to attract attention by arriving late. Few, if any, University clubs or societies were open to them. In all my undergraduate years I never spoke to anyone from a women's college, except in the most casual encounters at very occasional tea or tennis parties.

Undergraduate life

Most of the undergraduates in the first two categories mentioned here, and most from overseas, were paid for entirely by their own families. Those in the scholarship category had varying amounts of financial support from college scholarships, from well-endowed schools, or from 'county' scholarships. Most of the graduates from other universities were ineligible for college awards, but some had support from their own universities. There was more equity in the system than might appear. For most men, once they started earning, repaid their parents, helped to see other members of the family through the system, or expected in due course to pay for their own children to do so. Therefore the young men felt that the privilege of benefiting from the system committed them to obligations towards it. No one maintained that he had any 'right' to the benefits, nor that as a student he was in a job for which he had a right to be paid. And calling university or college authorities 'the management' would in those days have been a feeble joke in an undergraduate magazine.

As regards undergraduate life in general there was more attention to physical fitness, and less upon outstanding prowess in sport, than there is now. Unless committed to laboratory work, the normal thing was to take some form of outdoor exercise every afternoon. In those unenlightened times we still played games for fun. I played Rugby football, hockey, tennis and a little cricket, all very badly, and I did some cross-country running. If there was an afternoon when I happened not to be doing any of these, I would walk or bicycle for an hour or two. Many of us belonged to religious societies; few took much interest in politics, at any rate until we experienced the General Strike of 1926.

Our athletic (!) activities helped to determine the pattern of our day; they meant that we ate little for lunch, so breakfast (mostly provided by ourselves) was rather significant. Tea was the occasion for entertaining each other. Dinner in hall was by present-day standards gargantuan—soup, fish, entreé, joint, sweet and savoury every night; I believe I sometimes skipped the soup.

Dress was what seemed natural to us, but might strike modern youth as somewhat conventional. We wore college undergraduate gowns in hall, in lectures, in the University Library, in calling upon any senior member of the University, and both caps and gowns everywhere outside college after dusk, and surplices in Chapel. Going to London one always wore a suit, proper headgear and gloves; many wore spats as well and carried a rolled umbrella. In speech and writing I addressed any don as 'Sir' and anyone I knew only as another undergraduate simply by his surname; I should have to know a man in some other setting as well, e.g. in his family, before getting on Christian name terms with him.

It was a good life. Much of what I write will be critical about the course I followed; otherwise, for the purpose of the book, there might be little point in writing anything about it. But it would be wrong to give the impression that my friends and I were unhappy with what we were doing. Indeed I had little call to think back about the shortcomings of the way things were until I was asked to write this and one or two other accounts of them.

Tripos courses

I went up to Trinity College in 1923 as a scholar to read for the Mathematical Tripos. I followed the normal procedure of those times for anyone in my situation, which was to take the examination for Part I at the end of the first year, but to go straight into lectures for Part II.

The Part II examination at which I was aiming was to consist of the six compulsory papers in Schedule A, and the six papers for the optional Schedule B (which has now become Part III). We counted upon completing the lectures for Schedule A before the end of our second year. Of course we had to keep in practice with that work, but towards the end of the second year and throughout the third year we attended effectively only Schedule B lectures.

There was a currently approved syllabus for Schedule A—which I am pretty certain I never saw. It entailed attending about equal numbers of lectures in pure and in applied mathematics. This worked out at four courses per term, each of three hours per week (i.e. two hours per morning, since we had a six day week), for, I suppose, most of five terms. In mathematics in those days all such lectures were given by college lecturers in their own colleges—even if a college possessed no proper lecture rooms, when the lectures might be in the dining hall or in the library. One's timetable often demanded a bicycle trip of a mile or so to be accomplished in zero time between lectures. There was no department of mathematics. Apart from lectures and infrequent use of libraries, we did all our work in our own rooms. Every lecturer assumed we should buy whatever textbook he recommended for his course; the town's bookshops were well organised for the sale of second-hand copies.

It is hard to understand how Cambridge managed to maintain such a high reputation for mathematics when it taught mathematics so badly. I must suppose that Oxford did it even worse. The reform of the Mathematical Tripos has been a hardy perennial in Cambridge since before World War I. But successive 'reforms' have dealt with the syllabus and have done almost nothing about its teaching. In the years just after World War I much of the teaching of mathematics was still being done by men who had themselves taken the unreformed Tripos—up to 1909, the year after which the publication of the order of merit was abolished. Indeed I went to lectures given by at least four Senior Wranglers. Such men had been brought up while the tradition of the famous 'coaches' (like E J Routh) was still strong. Under that system almost everything had depended upon these coaches, and lectures evidently counted for relatively little. The reform of 1909 was in effect a revolt against what was left of that system. But for most Cambridge mathematicians some influence from it lingered on, actually—I would say—to the advantage of most undergraduates. On the other hand, a few of us were victims of too much reform.

In my time, and presumably ever since, some of the role of the former coaches was taken over by a man's college supervisor. The significant change was that the lectures had become the essential basis of the man's training and his supervisor was there to see that he got maximum profit therefrom. The supervisor had to see that his pupil went to what were for him the best available lectures in the most useful sequence and that he was keeping up with these lectures and any exercises set by the lecturer. The supervisor also got the man to do additional exercises for him, and they discussed the solutions. Above all he was someone with whom the man could discuss all aspects of his mathematical interests and aspirations. Although the lecturer had become a more significant element in the scheme of things than he had been in the old regime, he knew all the time that he was not the only one concerned; if he failed to put something across to someone in his class, he knew he could almost certainly rely upon that someone's supervisor making sure he got hold of that something.

I had no supervisor.

Of all undergraduates in all subjects in all colleges, only mathematical scholars (and possibly exhibitioners) in Trinity College, and so far as I know only in a few years around our time, were denied that advantage. Apparently we were guinea-pigs for some extremist who believed that if coaching had been wrong then every vestige of individual tuition must be wrong.

Every undergraduate had a College tutor who was responsible for seeing that each of his pupils fulfilled all the purely formal requirements of his academic status. He had nothing to do with the man's studies, except that in every normal case he would assign the man to a supervisor, or supervisors, who then took charge of his studies for the time being. Presumably the supervisor(s) periodically reported to the tutor about the student's progress. In the abnormal case of anyone in our peculiar category, our tutor assigned each of us to a 'director of studies'. This was a mathematician in the College who was a cut above the general run of supervisor. He seemed to have no responsibility except to have the undergraduate call upon him at the start of each term in order to be 'directed' to his lectures. I think he must have been under a vow not to offer tuition in any shape or form. In practice one first acquired a lecture list for the term and looked out courses that appeared to be intended for one's own stage. For each topic there were usually two parallel courses by different lecturers; one chose between these with the traditional pin. Also there were usually more topics than the routine four. So one avoided certain courses because one believed it to be possible to pick up enough about the subject by other means; for instance, I think I never heard a single lecture on differential equations. Others one avoided because it was popularly believed that they were a waste of time; although astronomy was in the Schedule A lecture list, somebody said to me that I should do better to devote myself to more important subjects. The astronomy concerned was indeed on rather formal aspects; actually I have always wished I had done it, but if I had it might have put me off ever wanting to do any more that was called 'astronomy'.

My own first director of studies was the great G I Taylor. At our first meeting I produced my lecture list and indicated the selection I had made along the lines I have just mentioned. He said 'All right' but he seemed altogether vague about what he was approving. Then he murmured 'Come and see me if you have a problem.' A week or two later I gave him the surprise of a lifetime by actually going to ask him about some simple problem in analysis. He smiled his charming smile, offered one or two vague suggestions, but said nothing about my coming again. He said 'All right' at the beginning of the next term or two and then moved to higher things—a Royal Society Professorship, I think. But that was beyond my ken in those days and it was only many years later that I discovered him to be a man of intelligence—about the most intelligent man of his generation! Then S Pollard took over the burden of directing my studies by saying his 'All right' once a term.

At the time I had no idea that my experience was in any way abnormal. I thought that things as I have tried to describe them were the Cambridge to which I had committed myself and that I just had to take it as I found it. I did get some impression that some of my friends in Trinity had a tutor, or a director of studies, who might be a trifle more human than mine. But in all my time as an undergraduate I never dreamt what a difference it would have made to have had a supervisor to talk to about my work. Actually, if I heard a mathematician from another college mention someone he called his supervisor, I thought this must be some arrangement he had to suffer because his college was perhaps not quite so good as Trinity.

Bicycling to lectures barely in time for the start, and away again as speedily as possible at the end, and having no department anywhere, meant that one scarcely came to know one's contemporaries as mathematicians. If students meet in a department they are almost bound to chat about what is going on there, to compare notes about lectures, lecturers, supervisors and so on. But if the same students meet a few hours later in a hockey match or in hall, they do not then talk shop.

In short, in all my undergraduate years I never once talked about mathematics with anyone senior to myself, and precious little with my contemporaries. Of course, I am glad that I escaped becoming dependent upon others. But there was no need to escape by such a wide margin; I did lose an enormous amount by not being able to discuss books, lecturers' merits, methods of work, and all the rest, with someone more experienced than myself. And if I had known the benefit of *receiving* that sort of help when I was a student, I am sure that in due course I should have been better at *giving* it to my own students.

Lectures and lectures

Most of the mathematics lecturers when I arrived in Cambridge dated from before World War I. Of these, the ones whose lectures I went to included J E Littlewood (Trinity) on infinite series, W Welsh (Jesus College) on analytical geometry, G Birtwistle (Pembroke) on dynamics, hydrodynamics, electricity and magnetism and E Cunningham (St John's) on electron theory. A few were starting to lecture after returning from war service; of these I heard S Pollard (Trinity) on mathematical analysis, R H Fowler (Trinity) on quantum theory, E A Milne (Trinity) on thermodynamics and kinetic theory of gases and L A Pars (Jesus College) on analytical dynamics.

There had been the famous post-war accumulation who had taken the Tripos in 1921. This included J C Burkill, W R Dean, E C Francis, A E Ingham, all of Trinity, M H A Newman of St John's and S W P Steen of Christ's College. These had all become dons about the time I went up: Burkill, Dean and Ingham in Trinity, Francis in Peterhouse, Newman in St John's and Steen in Christ's College, there being some subsequent moving around between Colleges. They themselves had all been taught exclusively by pre-war mathematicians, so their own first research tended to be in rather old-fashioned fields. I went to what I believe were the first courses given by Francis (algebra) and Dean (dynamics). In this context, it is interesting to note that those taking the Tripos after 1921, up to my own year, included F P Ramsey (1923), J D Cockcroft and L H Thomas (1924) and S Goldstein and W P D Hodge (1925). Those taking it in 1926 (my year) included W L Edge, J A Gaunt, N F Mott (Cavendish Professor 1954-71), R O Redman (Professor of Astrophysics 1947-72), H D Ursell and A H Wilson. This somewhat arbitrary selection of individuals and their rather well-known subsequent careers may give some indication of the way in which Cambridge mathematics, particularly on the 'applied' side, was edging into newer fields over the few years following World War I. Here may be the place also to mention some approximately contemporary mathematicians who in those years came to Cambridge as research students without taking the Tripos; these included P A M Dirac (St John's), H S W Massey (Trinity) and G F C Temple (Trinity).

To come back to the lecturers, among those I heard, Littlewood, Francis, Milne and Fowler appeared to enjoy their own lectures so that we had some inducement to enjoy them too. The others were bored or nervous and made little effort to carry their audience along with them. The general standard of presentation was uninspiring. Most lecturers at the end of a lecture sometimes dictated a few examples on the work we had just been through; they collected our solutions at the next lecture; at the one after that these were ready for us to pick up again, with a few ticks or crosses on them but generally no comments; the lecturers did not discuss these examples in the lectures. I think I found such exercises neither particularly interesting nor exacting.

After a rather ill-organised first term, I worked fairly faithfully to a self-imposed timetable that required me to do six hours serious work per day, including lectures, on six days a week. Apart from normal holidays, I worked about as hard in vacations as in term-time. In my second year, and afterwards as a BA, I 'kept' the 'long vacation term'; with the approval of one's tutor one was allowed to live in College for about five weeks from late June to about the end of July. There was dinner in hall and we had to be in College by 10 PM. There was non-serious tennis and cricket, and no lectures. But it was recognised to be a privilege to work under these conditions; this was not abused.

About the lectures themselves: I took notes straight into notebooks, and did not rewrite them. I fairly conscientiously mastered the main ideas of a lecture before hearing the next one in the course. But now I greatly wish that I had written out each lecture afresh. Thereby I should have arranged my ideas more systematically than I did, and I am sure I should have done a much better job when I came to write notes for lectures to my own students. I do *not* mean that I could have used my undergraduate notes on my students! But I should have trained myself in what good notes ought to look like.

Most of my work in vacations was working through my untidy notes, reading a bit more of the same work in the recommended textbooks and doing examples from these or from old Tripos papers (which were sold by the University at nominal cost). A very little of the right sort of advice from a supervisor would have enabled me to use all my time to far greater profit.

Schedule B of the Mathematical Tripos, Part II, was what has evolved into the present Part III. Apparently anyone could offer to deliver a one-term lecture course. If the appropriate Faculty Board approved, it would be announced in the Schedule B lecture list. This implied that in due time a candidate could declare a wish for there to be questions (probably two) on the course in the examination. A candidate could treat up to n courses in this way, where n was probably about six. If any candidate legitimately included a particular course in his list, the lecturer was responsible for producing the questions; these had then to be approved by the Part II Examiners, who had to arrange the Schedule B papers in such a way that every candidate's chosen subjects were suitably distributed through the six papers. But when it came to the examination any candidate could attempt any questions he liked; he need not confine himself to the topics in his list.

In the Part II examination there were six papers in Schedule A on three consecutive days in one week. These were set and marked by the six Examiners for the year, who awarded the Honours classes on the results. The six papers in Schedule B came a week later. The questions were marked by the individual setters and the marks were collated by the same six Examiners, who awarded a 'b*' for a pass with distinction, 'b' for what was called a 'pass' in Schedule B, or nothing for not passing.

Rightly or wrongly, the candidates believed that an average of four complete answers per paper in Schedule A and of about two good essays per paper in Schedule B would secure a first ('wrangler') and 'b*'. I suppose that supervisors advised their pupils on such points, but there was nobody to advise those in our category.

Neither did I have any guidance about what courses to take for Schedule B, not even to the minimal extent of choosing between pure and applied mathematics. Actually there was no compulsion to opt for one or the other, but I suppose I had enough wit to seek to make a selection of subjects that had some sort of coherence as a whole. It could indeed have been a vague impression that not very much that was new was coming up in pure mathematics that initially inclined me to the applied side at that stage. I can scarcely have had then much positive inkling of the pending revolution in mathematical physics.

The system I am trying to describe seemed to result in the bulk of the lecturing for Schedule A being done by men who at the time were in mid-career. In mathematics professors never lectured in Schedule A, and for that matter as an undergraduate I heard no single lecture by any professor of mathematics. The iniquity of this Cambridge practice came home to me when a little later I became a lecturer in the Mathematics Department in Edinburgh that was headed by its famous Professor, E T Whittaker. There every student who took any courses, however elementary, in his department had some lectures from the Professor himself. The student never forgot this for the rest of his life.

Some schedule B lectures, on the other hand, were given by the professors, some by Schedule A lecturers and some by very young dons lecturing upon their own special research interests. When I was a BA, for general interest I went to some lectures by Professor A S Eddington, which were attended also by some Schedule B candidates, but I had not heard him, or any other professor, before that. Eddington happened to be one of the two Moderators (senior examiners, in effect) when I took Part II, that being the nearest I had got to a professor of my own subject up to that time.

So far as I remember, the first Schedule B lectures I took were a course in Lorentz electron theory by E Cunningham and one in analytical dynamics by L A Pars. These I must have taken in my second year, because in the long vacation of 1925, as I clearly remember, I struggled to sort out the dynamics. It would have been wonderfully clever of Pars, had he foreseen that his subject was an essential basis for Dirac's quan-

tum mechanics, to which we were to be introduced in the following
year. But Pars did not know this; sadly for us, he preferred to follow a
presentation by the French mathematician Paul Appell to that in the
book by E T Whittaker, which was what Dirac used. I know I took that
particular course by Cunningham about the same time, and that I
found it dry and inelegant. However, it did turn out to provide a useful
background for learning some quantum theory, and this I started to do
in lectures by R H Fowler in the autumn of 1925. But I owe it to Cunningham, who undoubtedly knew what he was talking about, to record
that his lectures were much admired by some of my near contemporaries.

Under the title 'How quantum physics came to Cambridge' I have
recently described more of my Schedule B reading, followed by my
entry into research (*New Scientist* 17 October 1985 p 58–60). So I say
no more about it here.

Reflections

Disregarding the singularities of my own experience relative to the
general pattern of undergraduate mathematical studies when I was at
Cambridge, that pattern of lectures, tutorials, examinations, and even
quite a lot of the course, seems not to have changed in a fundamental
manner. Perhaps the most considerable changes have been in what is
classed as 'applied' mathematics. Mathematical 'methods', numerical
analysis, probability and statistics, and the like, have replaced some
traditional applied mathematics. Not altogether, but to a certain
extent, this must be owing to the universal availability of computing
facilities. Modern methods of information storage and access seem so far
not to have greatly affected undergraduate studies.

Changes that might have been expected have not materialised. For
instance, there surely ought to be a concise unified treatment of almost
all classical mechanics, including fluid mechanics, electrodynamics and
special relativity, at undergraduate level. There is not yet much sign of
this.

Again, in mathematics in contrast to most other subjects, it has
always been difficult to give undergraduates a glimpse of either the fron-
tiers of knowledge or of the foundations. Schedule B in our day was an
attempt to do this—perhaps the most effective one ever tried. In Cambridge this function is presumably taken over by Part III of the Tripos,
so that it seems to have become a somewhat less normal part of
undergraduate studies.

One significant change is illustrated by the fact that of the men who
took the Mathematical Tripos in my year, one (Mott) became Cavendish
Professor of Physics and Director of the Cavendish Laboratory, and

another (Redman) became Professor of Astrophysics and Director of the Cambridge Observatories. Until fairly recently in this country a good many physicists and nearly all astronomers have started as mathematicians. Contrary to this British tradition, in recent times university mathematics seems to have been withdrawing from the making of physicists and astronomers, to the detriment of British mathematics and British physical science.

CHAPTER SIX

AN ANGLO-SCOTTISH UNIVERSITY EDUCATION

G C McVittie

In the 1920s undergraduates entering the University of Edinburgh could embark on an Honours degree course leading after four years to a Master of Arts degree in Mathematics and Natural Philosophy. The course was principally a compound of pure and applied mathematics and of physics, experimental as well as theoretical. In addition, the student had to offer two subjects lying outside the domain of physical science. This was the curriculum on which I started in 1923 at the age of nineteen. I was therefore somewhat older than my classmates, a fact attributable to family financial troubles produced by one of the minor wars of the twentieth century.

Teaching was almost entirely by means of lectures, apart of course from the laboratory work in physics and certain tutorial classes. With the benefit of hindsight, I believe that the standard of lecturing must have been unusually high. Sir Edmund T Whittaker, the Professor of Pure Mathematics, was a past-master of the art. His highly polished style persuaded us, the students who listened to him, that every topic was easily comprehensible. A subsequent reading of one's notes showed that this was not so, at least, not until much further work was done. Among the junior staff was Edward T Copson, later to be Regius Professor of Mathematics in the University of St. Andrews, who also excelled in the lucidity of his lecturing methods. In contrast, Sir Charles Galton Darwin, the Tait Professor of Natural Philosophy, who lectured on applied mathematics, had a very untidy style. Nevertheless his asides on the nature of applied mathematics—and of applied mathematicians—and his obvious enthusiasm for the subject intrigued me. I often came away from one of his lectures having understood very little but determined to discover what my chaotic notes meant and what it was that aroused such interest in this man.

The Physics Department was headed by Professor C G Barkla who had been awarded in 1918 the Nobel Prize in Physics for the year 1917.

During the 1920s, and indeed to the end of his life, he was engaged in a fruitless search for experimental evidence in support of the 'J phenomenon'. It was intended to demonstrate that an atom possessed a shell of electrons interior to the K shell. He insisted that certain 'string and sealing-wax' experimental methods had to be used. When physicists in other laboratories tried to obtain his results with more up-to-date apparatus, they failed to do so. This led Whittaker to say to me once that he felt sure that the J phenomenon would one day prove to be due to the Edinburgh east wind! A more inspiring teacher was Dr H R Robinson, in later life Professor of Physics in Queen Mary College, London.

The University regulation that required me to take two optional subjects in the humanities was a fortunate one. One option gave me the opportunity of listening to Professor Norman Kemp Smith discoursing on Plato and Aristotle and more especially on Kant, Locke, Berkeley and Hume. To the doctrines of the last three philosophers I perhaps owe the germ of my attitude to mathematical physics, which many years later was to be described by S Mavridès (1973) as that of an uncompromising empiricist. The second option I chose was a course in economic history, which was taught by a Welshman whose name, as far as I can remember, was J F Rees. He would often enter the classroom accompanied by an enormous hound, some kind of Central European hunting dog. Telling us that the dog would not interfere with us and that we would not annoy him, Rees would start speaking in his soft Welsh voice. The dog would instantly fall asleep whilst we listened with rapt attention to the exposition of a subject that might seem on the face of it to be extremely dull. When in later years I heard that his faculty colleagues credited Rees with hypnotic powers, I had no difficulty in believing the story. Incidentally, I cannot remember being 'counselled' by any faculty member to select the two options I chose. Indeed when I went to ask Dr Rees if I might enrol in his course he asked me what had made me select it and he seemed gratified with my reply which was that I thought everyone ought to have some acquaintance with the economic development of the country.

The courses in physics and applied mathematics treated these subjects classically. They embraced topics such as classical dynamics, heat and light, thermodynamics, electricity, hydrodynamics and wave theory. Of course, a student who had chosen to work towards the Mathematics and Natural Philosophy degree did not take all courses offered in physics and applied mathematics. But it is curious that up to the time I graduated in 1927, I cannot remember hearing of any instruction in the modern physics of the time. For example, I discovered the Bohr atom by chance through picking up a book in the University Library. Copson told me something of wave mechanics when I asked him who this man

Schrödinger was and had he done anything in mathematical physics before propounding his wave equation. Copson assured me that he was already a well-known mathematician! All this is particularly odd in view of the presence of Darwin in the University. He had made contributions to atomic theory before coming to Edinburgh.

The situation in mathematics was somewhat different. As was to be expected from the co-author of *Modern Analysis*, Whittaker had organised a department in which the teaching of analysis in general and of the properties of special functions were prominent. But higher algebra and geometry were not neglected. Moreover Whittaker was one of the pioneers in offering instruction in numerical methods and statistics. He had a wide acquaintance among the actuaries working for the many insurance companies that existed in Edinburgh and it was they who inspired him to set up courses in numerical methods.

I have already remarked that in those days there was little advising of students. Each man or woman was supposed to know what they needed to learn and to pick their courses from their own interpretation of the course titles. It soon became the fashion among those students who fancied themselves as mathematicians to look down on the numerical methods courses, which were said to consist merely of doing arithmetic with the aid of enormous books of tables. I too suffered from these illusions and thus failed to take advantage of the instruction offered in statistical theory and its associated numerical methods. This proved to be a handicap throughout my professional life.

If I graduated from Edinburgh knowing little of the quantum theory, I did better with respect to the other new theory invented in the early part of the twentieth century, namely Einstein's theory of relativity. Whittaker lectured on the subject to final year undergraduates among whom I found myself in 1926–7. In addition it happened that from January to March 1927 Sir Arthur S Eddington delivered in Edinburgh the Gifford Lectures that were later published in his book *The Nature of the Physical World* (1928). A good part of this work is devoted to a verbal discussion of relativity which supplemented and illuminated Whittaker's mathematical exposition. In delivering these lectures, Eddington gave the impression that he was an expert and eloquent speaker. In spite of the instruction thus provided by two such eminent authorities, the cosmological implications of general relativity, at least, did not become readily obvious. One day, Jack Whittaker (John M Whittaker, in later life Vice-Chancellor of Sheffield University) told me his father had suggested that he should look into the possibility of interpreting through general relativity the red-shifts in the spectra of galaxies observed by 'someone called Hubble'. As far as I can remember nothing came of this suggestion.

There is little to be said about my undergraduate work in the physics laboratory in spite of the fact that I was a demonstrator in the laboratory for one year after graduation. We worked in pairs on the experiments and since my partner was an excellent practical experimenter I contented myself with doing any arithmetic or algebra that we needed in order to write up the experiment. How I succeeded in passing the final practical examination—which had to be done single-handed—after such reprehensible conduct, I cannot now explain.

Graduate work, which continued until June 1930, began with the year 1927–8 being spent in Edinburgh attending Whittaker's post-graduate lectures. They were concerned with field theories that attempted the unification of gravitation and electromagnetism. Then in October 1928 I entered Cambridge as a research student with Eddington as my supervisor. By this time quantum mechanics formed part of advanced teaching in physics at Cambridge and Eddington advised me to attend the lectures on the subject given by P A M Dirac. Dirac had shortly before completed his book on quantum mechanics and his lectures followed that text fairly closely. The class contained many Cambridge BAs who were now research students. It was apparently customary in Cambridge to ask a lecturer for further explanation of a point by saying 'Would you please repeat that, Sir?' One of the Cambridge men had occasion to try this on Dirac, who looked down at his notes and then repeated what he had just said in exactly the same words. A silence fell on the unenlightened class and further elucidations were never asked for again. Eddington also indicated that R H Fowler's lectures on statistical mechanics and G Birtwistle's on thermodynamics would do me no harm. Eddington's own course on the theory of stellar structure provided a considerable surprise. The eloquent and lucid Gifford Lecturer was replaced by an apparently confused and hesitant speaker who seemed to have a poor grasp of his subject! In later years I discovered that all Eddington's public lectures were read so skilfully from a written text that they seemed to be delivered extemporaneously.

Einstein was to reach the age of 50 in 1929 and it was rumoured that he would then announce a new all-embracing theory of physics. This proved to be the unified field theory of gravitation and electro-magnetism that employed the geometrical device of 'parallelism at a distance' which I had begun to study in Edinburgh. Eddington suggested that it would be interesting to find an exact solution of Einstein's field equations and do the same for the corresponding case using the 1929 field equations of his 1916 general relativity and compare the two results. It proved possible to carry out this programme for the gravitational field of an electric force, or of a magnetic force, of uniform direction. Incidentally it was possible to determine exactly what Einstein meant by his statement that the 1916 and 1929 theories gave 'approximately' the same results. A paper (McVittie 1929) on my conclusions was prepared and was submitted by Eddington to the *Proceedings of the Royal Society* on 6 May 1929. This paper and other investigations on various modifications of the theory of teleparallelism produced a thesis that earned me a Cambridge PhD in June 1930.

Preparation of this thesis was interrupted for some weeks in early 1930 by Eddington's suggestion that I should work on the theory of the redshifts of galaxies. He suspected that it would elucidate the problem of the stability or otherwise of the Einstein Universe. After some progress had been made the investigation came to an abrupt halt when one day Eddington, rather shamefacedly, showed me a letter from the Abbé G Lemaitre reminding Eddington that the problem had been implicitly solved in 1927 by Lemaitre himself (Lemaitre 1927). Eddington confessed that, though he had seen Lemaitre's paper in 1927, he had completely forgotten about it until that moment. The oversight was soon remedied by Eddington's notice in the 7 June 1930 issue of *Nature* (Eddington 1930a), as well as in other publications (Eddington 1930 b, c) in which he drew attention to Lemaitre's brilliant work.

This curious incident perhaps illustrates the differences between the conduct of science in the 1920s and today. The circulation of preprints and the 'Letters' journals had not been invented; scientific meetings were comparatively rare and funds for attending them were meagre; and the scientific journalist, ready to make the most of any new development, had yet to come to full flower. Thus it was possible for the paper that set the cosmology of general relativity on its way to lie unnoticed for three years. By a fortunate chance I was involved in its rebirth and was thus started on researches which occupied a good part of my professional life.

References

Eddington A S 1928 *The Nature of the Physical World* (Cambridge: Cambridge University Press)
—— 1930a *Nature* **125** 850
—— 1930b *Mon. Not. R. Astron. Soc.* **90** 668
—— 1930c *The Observatory* **53** 162–3
Lemaitre G 1927 *Ann. Soc. Sci. Brux.* **47**A 49
Mavridès S 1973 *L'Univers Relativiste* (Paris: Masson) p 7
McVittie G C 1929 *Proc. Roy. Soc. Lond.* A **124** 366

CHAPTER SEVEN

RECOLLECTIONS OF STUDENT YEARS IN GERMANY

H A Brück

The circumstances of my academic training in the Germany of the 1920s differed greatly from those at the present time and were quite distinct from the conditions in the United Kingdom. Anyone with a Leaving Certificate, an *Abitur*, of a certain standard in the Arts or Sciences, whichever he wished to pursue—and with sufficient financial support from home—was able to enrol in one or more universities of his choice and attend any courses in which he was interested. If he wished to attain in the course of four years or more the final stage of a Doctorate in physical science, he had to fulfil only one precondition: in the case of experimental science, that he had gained sufficient practical experience in the laboratory, and in the case of theoretical studies, that he had taken an active part in a certain number of Seminars in the Department. To gain a Doctorate a candidate was also expected, in Germany as everywhere else, to submit a thesis and to pass a fairly substantial oral examination in both his main and two subsidiary subjects.

I myself went to university from an old-style *Gymnasium*, in which Latin and Greek played a prominent role. My school was the '*Kaiserin-Augusta-Gymnasium*' in Berlin–Charlottenburg, which had a high reputation for the standard of its teaching. Latin and Greek were indeed taught so well that I still retain a great love of the Classics. However, the *Gymnasium* could also boast an outstanding teacher of mathematics and physics, the subjects in which I was particularly interested. The quality of the teaching was such that when I entered university I found not the slightest difficulty in competing with students who had come from more modern, science-orientated schools.

I attended three different universities in Bonn, Kiel and Munich, spending one semester, half a year, at each of them in a general exploration of conditions and deciding eventually on Munich, where I spent another five semesters before attaining my Doctorate. I started in May 1924 in the University of Kiel both for personal reasons and, being particularly interested in astronomy, I had met there C Wirtz who, ten years before E Hubble in America, was studying radial velocities of galaxies and trying to relate them to de Sitter's relativistic model of the Universe. Mathematics was taught in Kiel by H Hasse and a very attractive course in chemistry was provided by Diels, the later Nobel Laureate. For the winter semester of 1924–5 I went to Munich, where my hopes of profiting from H von Seeliger's work in stellar astronomy were dashed by his illness and death. In the summer of 1925 I transferred to the University of Bonn where one of the courses which I attended—together with Max Delbrück who later moved into biology—was given by K F Küstner, one of the leaders in the field of positional astronomy at the time. In the winter semester of 1925 I returned to the University of Munich where I stayed until I received my Doctorate in the summer of 1928.

There was some very good teaching by various members of the Science Faculty. In the beginning I concentrated on astronomy, which was then entirely devoted to classical celestial mechanics for which close knowledge of books by F Tisserand, H Poincaré and similar authors was considered absolutely essential. Though I managed to get on well in this field, I was quite overwhelmed when I came across the course in theoretical physics which was given by A Sommerfeld, by far the best university teacher I have ever met. His complete course extended over six semesters of which I was able to attend only four, but all of these were memorable. I remember with particular pleasure his lectures on partial differential equations of physics, which he started by talking about Fourier's *Théorie Analytique de la Chaleur*, 'the Bible of the mathematical physicist' as he used to call it. And then there were his marvellous lectures on the new wave mechanics which was coming to the fore at the time. I was busy preparing talks which I was asked to give on Schrödinger's papers in the *Annalen der Physik* in Sommerfeld's seminar. That was also the time at which Sir Arthur Eddington's *Internal Constitution of the Stars* appeared, a book in which Sommerfeld took a great interest.

With frequent visits of distinguished physicists from inside and outside Germany, a very happy atmosphere prevailed at all times in the Munich Department of Theoretical Physics which is quite unforgettable. I well remember Heisenberg's first enunciation of his 'Uncertainty Principle' in the Munich seminar in which K Bechert and A Unsöld were amongst prominent members of the younger generation. Personal relations were cemented at musical evenings in Sommerfeld's home and in particular in excursions to his little chalet in the Bavarian mountains where members of staff and senior students could exercise their skiing in the company of the Professor, who sometimes invited his friend Professor J Zenneck, who gave a highly acclaimed course on experimental physics at the Technical University in Munich. In the University itself experimental physics was represented by W Wien, of whom students were in considerable awe. In the oral examinations for my Doctorate I was the last student to be examined by Wien in experimental physics; he died in August 1928.

Having submitted a thesis on the computation of the forces in crystals as they follow from the use of wave mechanics I was awarded the degree of Dr Phil in July 1928 on the same day as Hans Bethe. He left Munich to teach at various other German universities before he went to England and later settled in the United States. I myself went on the recommendation of Professor Sommerfeld to the Einstein Institute, a Department of the Potsdam Astrophysical Observatory, which was then considered to be the most advanced in the country. Seven years later, in August 1935, I also received at the University of Berlin the higher degree of Dr Phil Habil, which was awarded on the strength of a sufficient number of research papers and following a statutory interval of seven years after the Dr Phil.

CHAPTER EIGHT

LEARNING AND TEACHING QUANTUM MECHANICS 1926–33: CAMBRIDGE, COPENHAGEN AND MANCHESTER

Sir Nevill Mott

I took the mathematical tripos at Cambridge in 1923. In those days a student took Part II, the examination on which he was classed, in both pure and applied mathematics, and at the same time Schedule B, which was optional and contained questions on specialised subjects with a wide choice. This has now become Part III and is taken in a subsequent year. Since my school days I had wanted to do research in theoretical physics, and among the subjects I took were relativity, statistical mechanics and electron theory of metals. Of course the first papers on quantum mechanics did not appear until 1926; I only vaguely remember a course on the old quantum theory, but the books by Sommerfeld and by Andrade are still on my shelves and I believe that questions were asked on their contents. The lecture course I remember most clearly was that by Ebenezer Cunningham of St John's College, actually my director of studies, on electrons in metals. The Hall effect showed that about one electron per atom was free in monovalent metals, we learned that the ratio of the electrical to the thermal conductivity could be predicted by theory, but the large value of the mean free path at low temperatures was a mystery, as was also the absence of an electronic specific heat. I remember asking the lecturer why electrons in metals were free and those in insulators stuck. Of course he did not know. This had to await quantum mechanics.

In 1926 it was clear that I had to learn quantum mechanics, and the only way to do it was to read the original papers. My German was rudimentary; I spent some of the Long Vacation in Germany and then, in October, set to work on the papers of Born, Heisenberg and Jordan and of Schrödinger. There were of course no lectures on the subject;

Ralph Fowler, who looked after theoretical physics, was on leave and the only man who fully understood the subject was Paul Dirac. I do not remember discussing the matter with him, although he was in the same college; perhaps we were both too shy. I did however read his paper on the Einstein A and B coefficients. Schrödinger's approach through differential equations, which I knew about, appealed to me more than that of Heisenberg or Dirac. When I came to look for a research problem, I was fully aware of the probability interpretation of the wave function $|\psi|^2 = N$, and that Schrödinger's interpretation was wrong. I owed this to Max Born's paper *Wellenmechanik der Stossvorgänge* (1926 Z. *Phys.* **37** 863) as well as to the experiments on electron diffraction, in view of which no other interpretation was really possible. I do not remember ever worrying about this—but I don't think anyone ever explained it to me.

When I went for a term to Niels Bohr in Copenhagen in the autumn of 1928, Dirac had already published his relativistic wave equation—the most beautiful exercise in pure reason that I have ever seen—and I had applied it to collision problems. In Copenhagen I had for the first time really close contact with a great scientist. I don't think Bohr taught me much about quantum mechanics—I knew it already—but what he taught me about the meaning of physics, and how to do research, was of infinite value. In Cambridge we worked in our college rooms, in comparative isolation; in Copenhagen we were in and out of each other's rooms all day, and so was Bohr. Theoretical physics was a social phenomenon. A letter to my parents, dated October 1928 says:

> Yesterday at four o'clock Bohr said, 'come across to my house and discuss the little bit of work that you have just done, and a bit of work rather similar of someone else's'; Bohr lives opposite the Institute. And at six it was supper time, and Bohr said stay for supper, and I had supper with him and his wife, and we talked about sculpture. And then after supper we went on discussing, and it became more and more Bohr and less and less me. And by about 9 we had got about as far with the problem as seemed possible without further calculations, and so Bohr began to talk about the Philosophy of the Quantum theory and how it was all bound up with the impossibility of man's knowing himself, and his not being able to know the external world completely because he himself was a part of the external world. And then back to the Quantum theory and the outstanding problems again. And about eleven we said good night.
>
> It is incredibly nice of him, isn't it, to give individual students this attention.
>
> He has got a brain. When he has a new idea—he had this morning—he comes into the Institute and tells it to the first person he can find; today that was me.
>
> Extraordinary what a difference it makes to life in general if one's work is going well. When I got messed up in that beastly arithmetic, and the

thing gave an answer that didn't agree with Rutherford's expts., one felt that one was stupid, would never do any good at this game, consequently rather overworked, and got dreadfully fed up and wondered if I'd better not come home and get a job like (my cousin) Johnny Simmonds. But now all goes well.

I like the life here where half one's work is discussing. That is the great point of Copenhagen I believe—though its probably the same in Germany too. Only Bohr knows <u>everything</u> that's being done, and has a marvellous knack of finding the sense behind mathematics.

Bohr is the kind of man who can tell one that one is talking nonsense, without hurting—I don't think one can say more than that, do you?

And he has his students alone in the evening to talk, and then walks home with them, telling how he discovered his theory of spectra.

And then it's 1 a.m. perhaps.

But it is funny that the spin of the electron can never be observed, isn't it? Perhaps the spin is only an illusion.

In the autumn of 1929 it was time to get a job, and I was fortunate that one was available at the University of Manchester, as theorist to W L Bragg's department. My chief task was to give a course of lectures on quantum mechanics to staff as well as students. Whether it was successful I cannot judge, but a letter to my parents records that one of the older researchers told me that he had never realised there was anything aesthetic in mathematics till after my lecture. I was pleased. The content of the lectures was incorporated in my first book, *An Outline of Wave Mechanics*, published by the Cambridge University Press in 1930.

In the autumn of 1930 I returned to Cambridge and gave in the Cavendish a course of lectures, in the Michaelmas Term on quantum theory, in the Lent Term on wave mechanics. The first term I did it my audience melted away; perhaps they knew it already. But in the Lent Term, lecturing on wave mechanics I managed to hold them.

CHAPTER NINE

PHYSICS IN CAMBRIDGE IN THE LATE 1920s

F A B Ward

My formal training in physics began at Highgate School, London, and my physics master was O W Dumaresq, a good and painstaking teacher whom I admired for his complete scientific honesty and integrity. I remember especially that on occasions when I asked him a difficult question he would immediately reply 'I don't know the answer to that, but I will look it up', and he *did* so and gave me the answer in the next class. The physics laboratories were rather small and without expensive equipment, but in spite of this I notice from my written-up notebook that I performed 57 experiments during the year beginning October 1921, many of them, of course, quite elementary.

Undergraduate: 1924–7

At Cambridge, my first year lectures on light, sound and heat were given by Alexander Wood of Emmanuel College and I immediately began to revel in them. He was a friendly Scot with a fine but not excessive sense of humour; his delivery was excellent and the experiments he performed on the lecture bench were ingenious, instructive and memorable. Electricity and magnetism lectures were by C D Ellis (later Sir Charles Ellis) and were also excellent. The first year physics laboratory work was under the supervision of Dr G F C Searle, a remarkable and strong character. Searle was bearded and of rather formidable appearance and spoke somewhat quickly, but this exterior concealed great wisdom, a penetrating mind and a subtle sense of humour. I remember his pointing out the importance of first taking a careful zero reading, remarking that 'some people don't realise that a length has *two* ends'!

For Part I of the Natural Sciences Tripos I took three subjects, physics, chemistry and mathematics, but for Part II, a one-year course, I took physics alone. I now still have before me the notes of three important sets of lectures I attended during this year and you will see, as I outline them, that the then 'new physics' appeared in them strongly (figure 9.1).

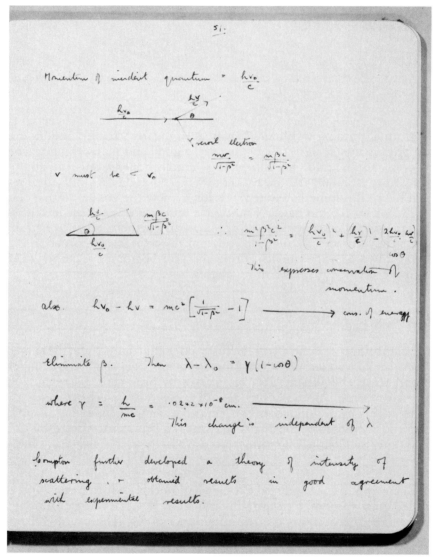

Figure 9.1 Dr Ward's notes on Compton's theory of x-ray scattering (1923) in the Part II Physics course of 1926.

Thermionics and x-rays

These subjects were covered by Mr G Stead, a lecturer with a cool, calm manner and a crisp diction. He began with the early experiments of Elster and Geitel and the Edison effect, followed by O W Richardson's theory. Then came Langmuir's theory and Dushman's experiments, also those of Wehnelt and J J Thomson and, later, of Franck and Hertz and K T Compton.

On x-rays the lectures followed an orderly course through the work of Röntgen, Coolidge, Laue, Friedrich and Knipping and, at considerable length, of Moseley and the Braggs. Here I must make a diversion to refer to a later lecture I heard from Rutherford on experimental methods in general. He was impressing on his hearers the importance of 'doing rough experiments first' before proceeding to very accurate measurement. Moseley, he pointed out, in investigating the x-ray spectrum, set up an accurate spectrometer with a rather narrow slit and carefully plotted the continuous spectrum, but he altogether missed the lines, whereas Bragg 'went round with a tin can and found them at once!'. In his x-ray lectures Stead continued by explaining Bohr's theory of the origin of the lines. He continued with accounts of the work of Crowther and A H Compton and of Barkla on the 'J phenomenon', only just published at the time of his lectures.

Physics of the quantum theory

This was dealt with by D R Hartree, the well-known theoretical physicist who was a competent but not exciting lecturer: these lectures were given in the early months of 1927. After a preliminary study of statistical mechanics, Hartree proceeded to Bohr's theory of atomic spectra, to the quenching of resonance radiation, sensitised fluorescence, thermal excitation and ionisation, followed by a detailed consideration of the numerical application of quantum theory to atomic structure, including the effect of magnetic fields on orbits, the Zeeman effect, the spinning electron, and dealt with band spectra, rotation and vibration.

The Structure of Matter

I was privileged to attend a long series of lectures on this subject by Rutherford himself. He was definitely a good lecturer, with a very natural manner; on all aspects of any branch of the subject he simply told us the story, well-illustrated on the blackboard, and on the particular fields of atomic and nuclear physics, to which he had made such great contributions himself, his warm enthusiasm was infectious; he also had a great sense of humour entirely without malice and was a good raconteur. From my extensive notes I can here only summarise the range of the subjects he covered.

He began with estimates of the size of molecules by Thomas Young, by Kelvin from the stretching of fluid surfaces and from the kinetic theory of gases, following Maxwell. Rutherford referred to the year 1895 as marking the birth of the 'new physics', for in that year Röntgen discovered x-rays, in 1896 Becquerel discovered radioactivity and in 1897 J J Thomson discovered the electron. He mentioned, incidentally, that the invention of the mercury vacuum pump in 1870 paved the way for much vital research on the electrical discharge in gases, as it enabled a much higher vacuum to be obtained than previously. Perrin had shown that cathode rays carried a negative charge and Lenard that they could penetrate a thin film.

Rutherford next proceeded to discuss work on the unit of positive electricity (this was, of course, before the discovery of positrons). From quite early days it became probable that alpha-particles from radium were atoms of hydrogen or helium. For helium e/m should be 4823 emu (electromagnetic units) and in 1913 Rutherford and Robinson obtained an experimental value of 4826 for alpha-particles. Rutherford then referred in passing to methods of detecting single alpha-particles by (a) string electrometer, (b) Geiger counter, (c) scintillations and (d) Wilson cloud chamber. He always, I found later, took a particular delight in the cloud chamber, because it confirmed, visually and accurately, so many of the results he himself had obtained by other methods. The application of thermionic valve circuits to amplify the small ionisation effects produced by single alpha-particles was pioneered, after these lectures I am describing, by Greinacher, and I myself, with Dr C E Wynn-Williams, played some part in helping to introduce this method to the Cavendish Laboratory (Hendry 1984).

The next subject in Rutherford's lectures was again the *sizes* of atoms and molecules, referring to diffusion and the Brownian movement. Then followed a group of lectures concerned with the structure of atoms themselves and of this he gave a masterly and extensive survey, which I can summarise only briefly. Rutherford began by describing Kelvin's 'positive sphere' atom, followed by J J Thomson's planar ring model. Definite information came from the scattering of alpha-rays leading, of course, to Rutherford's own nuclear atom. Next came evidence of the structure of the nucleus, referring to isotopes and positive rays. The lectures now switched to quantum theory and its applications to atomic and nuclear structure, and this was followed by a wide-ranging survey of ionisation and the conduction of electricity through gases (my notes on these lectures cover 42 pages!). In the final series of lectures Rutherford dealt with radioactivity and the properties of alpha-, beta- and gamma-rays.

Concurrently with these lectures the syllabus of work in the final year preceding the Part II physics examination covered a wide range of experiments in the laboratory using what was for those days fairly sophisticated apparatus. From my notebooks I append a list of 17 such experiments, in which a high degree of carefulness and accuracy was expected (see appendix to this Chapter). Mr H Thirkill of Clare College was in charge of this class. He was a quiet, firm, wise and much respected man.

Some Thoughts on Student Funding and Jobs

The following notes are very general and derive from somewhat fading personal memories. They lack precision but may, I hope, be of some interest.

Undergraduate scholarships

Well-endowed schools offered scholarships in the region of £60 to £80 per annum. I was fortunate to have one. I do not think that Local Authorities gave as many as nowadays. Cambridge Colleges offered scholarships of about the same value, also *exhibitions* of about £40. Groups of about five colleges conducted examinations, held in Cambridge in early December. I applied for Gonville and Caius, but was offered one by Sidney Sussex, which I gratefully accepted. College scholarships lasted for the full three years' degree courses.

For postgraduate research students, some colleges allowed undergraduate scholarships to continue for two further years. The Royal Commission for the Exhibition of 1851 offered overseas studentships. The Goldsmith's Company of London also offered studentships for two years.

Jobs situation for new graduates

Perhaps about half of physics graduates went into teaching. About one-quarter continued at Cambridge with physics research. About one-quarter went into industry or similar jobs. In 1927, jobs in general were reasonably easy to obtain. In 1931, when I was job-hunting, the Great Depression was just beginning and jobs became fewer. I was appointed an Assistant Keeper in the Science Museum in that year; two years later, in 1933, the Depression was in full swing and another job of the same rank as mine, at the Science Museum, became vacant. There were 80 qualified applicants, including 15 PhDs. The job went to one of these, a graduate of Oxford. War was not really in sight as early as this.

Postgraduate: 1927–31

It was a most fortunate day for me personally when Rutherford decided that I should work with Eryl Wynn-Williams on the application of radio

valve amplifiers to the detection of individual alpha-particles. I was a
first year researcher but Eryl had already carried out research (not in
nuclear physics) in Bangor and at the Cavendish Laboratory. He was a
very knowledgeable and skilful operator in the field of valve amplifiers
for radio and other uses, and he designed the amplifier which we used,
in collaboration with H M Cave, in determining, by direct counting, the
rate of emission of alpha-rays from radium. We used a modified form
of this amplifier in later researches, with Rutherford himself, on the
alpha-rays from RaC, ThC and AcC. For these, Eryl constructed a simple
but very effective moving-magnet mirror oscilloscope of rapid response,
to replace the string galvanometer we had earlier used.

While this work was in progress we had a short visit from an American
physicist who brought with him and demonstrated to us a thyratron.
Eryl was thrilled with this and at once realised that thyratrons could be
used for fast counting. He built a 'scale of two' thyratron counter and
also a 'ring of 10' counter. This, I believe, was the decisive first step in
the whole now vast range of electronic computers.

It gives me the utmost pleasure to pay a warm tribute to Eryl Wynn-
Williams on the personal side. He immediately befriended me and I
could not have wished for a more congenial fellow worker. This was in
keeping with his whole character and, I believe, this showed to very
great advantage in his later relations with the many students to whom
he taught practical physics when he became an Associate Professor in the
Imperial College of Science and Technology in London.

I had the good fortune to work in actual collaboration with Lord
Rutherford (see the paper by Rutherford *et al* (1931)) for two years
(1929–31) and to have closer contact with him after having listened, as
described above, to his lectures. With his great initiative and intuition
went a great zest and capacity for hard work. At the time I was working
with him, when he was aged about 60, his daily routine was to arrive
at the Cavendish Laboratory, on foot, at about 9.30 AM and work there
in his office on administration and tour the laboratory to talk to and
discuss with those who were researching there. He left about 1.15 PM,
returned from lunch before 3.00 PM and continued, as in the morning,
up to about 6.00 PM. He then left to return home to dine or to dine at
his College, Trinity. He then began his *real* work, as he would probably
express it, for I believe that on almost all weekday evenings he retired
after dinner to his study at home, I believe for several hours, to work
at his desk on his own work just on *physics* and not administration.

He was far from unmindful of political and world affairs, and about
once a week he had to spend the day in London attending meetings.
He regarded this as a duty to be carried out rather than as a break to
be enjoyed, though he was far from being unsociable. I remember that
on one occasion he came to my workroom on the following morning at

about 9.30 AM, sat down rather heavily and remarked 'Ah, Ward, it's hard work getting your own way—but I generally manage to do it!'

With his passion for work and results, he drove his research students hard; but if anyone was in real trouble he understood and was compassionate. On rare occasions, on calling on a research student after he had been away for several days, he would open his remarks impatiently with the words 'well—how have you been getting on with the marking time while I have been away?'

He enjoyed research conferences held in the laboratory with visiting physicists, and at such conferences his first public remarks were sometimes slightly fumbling, but after a few minutes his natural exuberance returned swiftly and he at once became a compelling speaker. He studied very carefully the results obtained by other workers in the same field as his, and when their results differed widely from his, as in the case of the artificial disintegration of atomic nuclei, he expressed surprise but no disdain or resentment. In public reference to other workers, from the present or past, I always noted his immense respect for Madame Curie, a respect amounting almost to deference. He also greatly respected the brilliance of mind of Chadwick, his Deputy Director of Research at the Cavendish Laboratory who was, only a few years later, to discover the neutron. In conclusion, I must repeat that it was a remarkable privilege and experience for me to be associated so closely, for a spell, with a man of Rutherford's calibre.

Cavendish Students

At the Cavendish Laboratory between 1927 and 1931 there was great camaraderie, and the British rejoiced in the company of those from overseas, including Canada, Australia, New Zealand and India. I myself, of course, knew very well, liked and respected my actual collaborators, Wynn-Williams, Cave and Lewis, my fellow graduates from Sidney Sussex College, Ratcliffe, Dee, J G Wilson and Moon, and also Constable, Pollard, Sargent, Webster, Chaudhuri and Malurkar (a theoretician). In the physics laboratories during my undergraduate period there were about 4 women among, say, 25 men; I think only one or two of these took physics as their final subject.

I had the pleasure of 'demonstrating' to E C Bullard under H Thirkill, in the third year practical physics course for undergraduates, and it was at once obvious that here was a person of almost unlimited capability. His was an extrovert, outgoing nature, delighted to explore anything with great energy and enthusiasm and to pursue it if promising. I was not surprised to see that his career was 'untidy', for he rose quickly to the top in administration and then stepped back, with very fruitful results, into new and different fields of more pure research. His temperament and joy in life were somewhat similar to those of Rutherford himself.

Appendix 9A: The Part II Physics Practical Class

My written-up laboratory notebook contains accounts of 17 experiments I carried out during the year's work. I now list these.

    (i) The surface tension of water and its variation with temperature. This was measured by observing the pressure head necessary to keep the water–air meniscus in a capillary tube at a given depth below the surface of the water

   (ii) Frequency of a tuning-fork, measured by comparing it with the frequency of an electrically maintained fork and phonic wheel.

  (iii) Measurements on coronas, produced round an illuminated pinhole by lycopodium particles sprinkled on a glass screen.

  (iv) Coefficient of viscosity of water, measured by observing the rate of flow of the liquid through a fairly small-bore tube.

   (v) Rotativity of a sugar solution, examined by a polarimeter.

  (vi) Rotation of quartz, with a polarising and an analysing nicol.

 (vii) Birefringence of selenite.

(viii) Five sets of observations with a ballistic galvanometer.

  (xi) Para- and diamagnetism, in aluminium and bismuth.

   (x) Selective dispersion of cyanine, in the form of a prism of small angle, pressed between a pair of glass plates.

  (xi) Distance apart of thin plates, by Fabry–Perot method.

 (xii) Distance apart of thin plates, using a banded spectrum.

(xiii) Dispersion of paraffin, using thin plates.

(xiv) Distance apart of thick plates, and more accurate determination of the wavelength of the helium yellow line.

 (xv) Radioactivity: absorption of heterogeneous beta-rays in aluminium, using a gold-leaf electroscope.

 (xvi) Radioactivity: decay of an active deposit of actinium.

(xvii) The Quadrant Electrometer: (a) adjustment; (b) variation of sensitivity with needle potential; (c) voltage sensitivity; (d) variation of ionisation current with voltage in an ionisation chamber.

References

Hendry J 1984 *Cambridge Physics in the Thirties* (Bristol: Adam Hilger) p 103–25, 133–49

The two publications in which my name appears jointly with that of Lord Rutherford were as follows:

Rutherford, Lord, Ward F A B and Lewis W B 1931 Analysis of the long-range alpha-particles from radium C *Proc. R. Soc.* A **131** 684–703

Rutherford, Sir Ernest, Ward F A B and Wynn-Williams C E 1930 A new method of analysis of groups of alpha-rays (1) The alpha-rays from radium C, thorium C and actinium C *Proc. R. Soc.* A **129** 211–34

CHAPTER TEN

UNDERGRADUATE IN PARIS 1926–8: GRADUATE STUDENT AND DR PHIL IN BERLIN, 1928–31

N Kurti

When I listened to Sir Samuel Curran talking about Scottish education, I felt so much at home. I come from Hungary and received my primary and secondary education in Budapest. Hungarian education and, in fact, Central European education was in those days akin to Scottish education and completely different from that in England. The intense specialisation often beginning at 13 or 14 was unknown in Hungary. I went to a *Gymnasium* of the 'humanistic' type, which meant that in addition to Hungarian, German, maths, history (Hungarian and World), biology, chemistry, physics and philosophy we had eight years of Latin and four of Greek. In the school-leaving examination at the age of 18 we were examined in Hungarian language and literature, in Latin, German, Greek and in mathematics, physics and history—in most cases on the syllabus of several years.

The result was that, although I had a good general education, I did not have the same sort of preparation that people have in England on entering university. This was particularly true for my chosen subject, physics. However, I was fortunate in getting excellent advice from a family friend, a physicist working in the research laboratory of the Tungsram Incandescent Lamp factory in Budapest, Dr Jacob Salpeter (father of Professor Edwin Salpeter, a theoretical physicist at Cornell University). He advised me to go first to Paris and get a good grounding in physics and more generally in science at the Sorbonne, i.e. the part of the university of Paris comprising the Faculté des Lettres and the Faculté des Sciences. (Today Paris has 10 or 12 universities.) It was easy to matriculate—you were admitted if you had the French Baccalaureat or its foreign equivalent—and there were no fees. However, no one I knew in Hungary had any idea of how the system worked: lectures, examinations, degrees.... But luckily I had an introduction to the famous physicist Professor P Langevin, at that time Director of the Ecole de Chimie et Physique de la Ville de Paris, one of the prestigious 'Grandes Ecoles'. (The present Director is Professor de Gennes.) He received me with great kindness and explained that I would be wasting my time if I just went to lectures without the discipline that working for an examination imposes upon you. He advised me to work for the degree of *Licencié ès Sciences Physiques* which was awarded on the basis of examinations in three subjects (*'certificats'*) and corresponded roughly to our BA. I chose, as did most of those who wanted to become physicists or chemists, *Mathématiques Générales*, *Physique Générale* and *Chimie Générale*. This gave me a good grounding in mathematics, physics and chemistry.

Lectures were formal, given before large audiences, often several hundred students. They were well-prepared, impeccably delivered and frequently illustrated with experiments. They were also 'meaty' and eight hours of lectures per week was probably the most one could cope with. Not only the lectures but also the professors' attire were formal. Thus Ch Fabry (of Fabry–Pérot fame), an excellent lecturer with an engaging manner, always appeared in black coat, striped trousers and grey waistcoat, while A Cotton (of the Cotton–Mouton effect) lectured in a frockcoat. A Guillet, a lively and enthusiastic lecturer, wore a shabby morning coat covered with layers of chalk. He was not at all the conventional and distant professor. He knew many of the regular atten-ders of his lectures by sight and I recall how one day he spotted me on the Boulevard St Michel in the Quartier Latin and asked me how I was getting along. I confessed that I was having some difficulties with his last lecture so he said 'I'm just taking a taxi to the Gare de l'Est. Hop in and I'll explain it.' 'Classical' physics was well-covered in the syllabus but there was precious little about post-1900 physics. Thus we heard only little about the Bohr atom, or quanta or relativity.

The practical classes (*travaux pratiques*) were good. They consisted of set experiments: everything was laid out and you had to assemble the apparatus and carry out the measurements, helped by very good explanatory notes on them. You had to do sixteen experiments per term (two four-hour sessions per week) and at the end of the term you could present yourself for a so-called partial exam where you had to carry out one of the experiments done during the term, but without any notes or notebooks. If you passed the three *partielles* you were excused from the final practical examination. The examinations were usually taken in July although there was also a session in late September. The important part of the examination was the written one, which in mathematics and in physics consisted of problem-solving, and there were no choices. In a four-hour examination one had to tackle two papers; thus for physics I had one in thermodynamics and one in optics. The preparation for the exam consisted in working over the lectures and solving problems. One bought excellent collections of problems—with solutions given in detail—taken from examinations held in earlier years.

In my first year at the Sorbonne I studied mainly for the *Mathématiques Générales* examination which I passed in July 1927. However, I did the physics practicals as well and some of the physics lectures. The year 1927–8 was devoted to *Physique Générale* and *Chimie Générale*. I obtained my *Licence* in July 1928 after two years. Considering my rather patchy preparation this was not bad. The failure rate for each examination was 60–80 %—but one could present oneself at every June and September session *ad infinitum*. I believe that the story of being given an automatic pass after 15 attempts is apocryphal.

In October 1928 I matriculated in the Friedrich–Wilhelm University (now Humboldt University) in Berlin to study advanced physics and to work for a Doctorate. In 1928–9 I just attended lectures and classes in physics and mathematics. There were no examinations and in fact in Germany one could spend five years of university studies without passing *any* examinations at all until one reached the Doctoral examination. There was a glittering array of professors in Berlin at that time—I mention only those whose lectures I attended: Planck, Schrödinger, Pringsheim, Ladenburg, Simon and von Laue. Planck was very clear and rather dry and you left the lecture thinking that you understood everything—and then later it dawned upon you that while everything was apparently made clear you still did not see the physics. von Laue was a poor lecturer but he ran good problem or exercise classes. Schrödinger was brilliant, the best of the lot. His statistical mechanics lectures were both instructive and stimulating and he often illustrated his lectures with the results of modern experimental work. It was his account of the then recent Leyden experiments, showing that the magnetisation of gadolinium sulphate follows Langevin's law as derived from statistical mechanics, which persuaded me to do a Doctorate in low-temperature magnetism. Although I became a graduate student a few years after the establishment of quantum mechanics and wave mechanics, we only felt the ripples of these developments. In quantum theory our staple diet was Sommerfeld's *Atombau und Spektrallinien* (Atomic Structure and Spectral Lines).

I did my Doctorate in 1929–31 in the Physical Chemistry Laboratory under F E (later Sir Francis) Simon, at that time an Associate Professor. I spent most of my time in the lab, occasionally attending some courses of lectures, but I went regularly to what seemed to me the most thrilling institution in Berlin physics, namely the famous Laue colloquium held every Wednesday between 5 and 7 PM in the Physikalisches Institut, the University's physics laboratory of which Nernst was at that time the Director. At the beginning of the century Nernst was Professor of

Physical Chemistry, then, immediately after the 1914–18 war, he became President of the German National Physical Laboratory (Physikalisch Technische Reichanstalt) and then went back to the University as Professor of Physics.

These colloquia, organised by von Laue, were rather like the American 'Journal Clubs'. Every week three or four speakers reported on one or two recent publications each, and normally everyone including graduate students was expected to volunteer for this task. The colloquia were held in a small, intimate lecture room comprising four or five rows in a raised tier, each one seating about 20 to 25 people. In the front row one would see Nernst, Einstein, Planck, Schrödinger and G Hertz, all Nobel Laureates, and then further on Pringsheim, Grotrian, Ladenburg, Simon etc, then came the 'small fry', Wigner, von Neumann, Szilard, F London, and so on and then assistants and research students. For a research student to address such an audience and to review critically for their benefit the work of some renowned physicist could be a daunting, but always exhilarating, experience. I volunteered to report on two papers on ferromagnetism, published in 1930 in *Philosophical Magazine*, one by E C Stoner and the other by a certain J R Ashworth. I managed to review Stoner's paper without appearing to be patronising, but when it came to Ashworth's paper I plucked up courage and was pretty scathing about it since to me it seemed merely trivial playing around with numbers. Fortunately the audience seemed to agree with me.

It was comforting for a young physicist occasionally to notice at these colloquia that even the great have their little lapses. I remember Fritz London once reporting on a theoretical paper about the rotational spectra of polyatomic molecules by R Mecke. For the calculation the atoms were regarded as points. During the discussion Schrödinger intervened saying that for triatomic molecules a simpler formula could be derived if one assumed that the three atoms are in the same plane. There was a stunned silence followed by a ripple, and then a roar of laughter in which Schrödinger joined in.

It was an indication of the 'size' of physics around 1930 that one person, namely von Laue, could pick out per week an average of four to six really important papers from the whole physics literature. But in those days relatively few periodicals had to be consulted: *Zeitschrift für Physik, Physikalische Zeitschrift, Proceedings of the Royal Society, Philosophical Magazine, Physical Review* and, most importantly, the letters sections of *Nature* and *Naturwissenschaften*. Furthermore if one attended the Laue colloquia regularly one obtained a good idea of what was new in physics.

In Germany in those days, unlike in Britain or in France, you did not have to pass any examinations until you got to your Doctorate. But then you had oral examinations in four subjects. I handed in my thesis 'On the thermal and magnetic behaviour of gadolinium sulphate' in June 1931 and for the oral examination I chose experimental physics and theoretical physics as main subjects, chemistry and philosophy as subsidiary subjects. At the Universities of Berlin and Halle philosophy was compulsory for DrPhil candidates. Although you could be asked questions about the *whole* of the chosen subjects—and indeed you were— the philosophy examination for scientists was made less exacting. In accordance with the custom, several months before the *viva* I went to see my philosophy examiner, Professor Wolfgang Koehler, who told me what books to read for the exam: one on the history of philosophy, one on epistemology and his own book on Gestalt psychologie.

For the exam you were closeted with your examiner, one hour each for the two main subjects and half an hour each for the subsidiary subjects. I had Nernst for experimental physics, Schrödinger for theoretical physics and Bodenstein for chemistry. Nernst appeared to be well satisfied with my performance because he showed me what he had written on the form: *'Vorzüglich, der Kandidat blieb keiner Antwort schuldig'* (Excellent, the candidate answered all the questions). I also caught a glimpse of Schrödinger's mark; it was *'Sehr gut'* (Very good). I think I did well in philosophy, but I did not cover myself with glory in chemistry. Nevertheless, I got my doctorate *magna cum laude*. I do not think that even if I had done well in chemistry I would have been given the top grade, *summa cum laude*, since it was generally believed that only poor students and sons or daughters of university professors got that distinction. The explanation was that anyone with a *summa* got *all* his University fees returned, but since those in the above two categories did not pay any fees their *summa* did not cost the University anything. This was the end of the beginning of my career as a physicist.

CHAPTER ELEVEN

THE EDUCATION OF PHYSICISTS BETWEEN THE WARS

H Fröhlich

The situation at that time was completely different from what it is now. The number of physicists was very much smaller, and relations were much more personal. It is best, perhaps, that I relate my own experience, although that was somewhat exceptional in that I took my PhD three years after entering the University of Munich as an undergraduate.

I became interested in physics through the development of the radio, but considered this as a hobby and entered business as a profession. In 1927, however, I decided to become a physicist. Posts in theoretical physics, however, were very scarce and most of those who studied it became teachers at schools. I therefore decided to study experimental physics with W Wien in Munich. I was unaware that I should have discussed this with him, or someone else. But having lost three years I thought that the most important thing was to find a subject for my Doctoral thesis.

At that time, a list of lectures which you could attend was available, one of which, entitled 'Problems in Physics', seemed particularly suitable. This turned out, however, to be a weekly physics colloquium. I went early and sat in the first row so as not to miss anything, which turned out to be very embarrassing. For a hierarchy existed such that the first row was reserved for the most senior professors and I as a first year undergraduate should not have been there at all, or at best in the last row.

Certain regulations existed according to which one had to 'book' and pay for a minimum of lectures and practicals. For reasons which I have forgotten, I enscribed in a course on chemistry practicals where you were to carry out experiments. This course was supervised by a chemistry PhD student who at the same time worked on his thesis. For this he had to make use of a sensitive galvanometer which he could not handle. I showed him how to use it and in return he signed my chemistry experiments for the whole year. As a consequence I never went there again—and did not learn any chemistry.

By the end of the year W Wien had died and I decided, in my second year, to attend Sommerfeld's principal course of lectures, which was one of his three-year courses. I did not know, at that time, that his was the world's leading institute. His course of lectures has become very famous, of course, but was published only after his death. In his lectures he did not use a manuscript but derived everything on the blackboard. In the course of this he sometimes made mistakes. One learned real theoretical physics from the way he noticed that he had made a mistake, and from the manner in which he found it.

I was able to follow his derivations, and when he made a mistake, next time, I interrupted him to tell him. This happened again, and he told me to remain after the lecture. This I did, and he said 'you will now direct the problem class'. Thus in my second undergraduate year I already had a post—though unpaid—as theoretical physicist. It should be mentioned that it was not unusual for Sommerfeld to pick people for advanced tasks while they were still undergraduates. Setting the problems, which I discussed with him and others before passing them to the students, really taught me theoretical physics. Of course, I studied quantum mechanics privately by reading original papers.

At the end of the year (my second undergraduate) Sommerfeld gave me a reprint which he had just received. During the holidays I found that I could make different calculations on the same subject and when I returned from the holidays I showed these to Sommerfeld. 'This is your thesis', he suggested, though a number of changes had to be made. At the end of my third undergraduate year I thus took my PhD. Clearly regulations nowadays would prohibit taking a PhD without having first taken an undergraduate degree. In 1930, however, this was possible although it involved some amusing incidents. Thus after submitting a thesis an oral examination had to take place, one hour on the main subject and two half-hours on subsidiaries. One of these, obviously was mathematics and for the other I chose physical chemistry. I had to visit the professor, who objected when he learned that I had not booked any of his lectures (for which he would have been paid) and was only in the third year. 'Always the gentlemen from theoretical physics' he said. When the day of my oral arrived, Sommerfeld remarked that he was very busy and that I should sit the hour alone. He did come in at the end, avoiding another remark on the 'gentlemen from theoretical physics'.

In the following year I had a research grant, but half-way through I had to move to the Institute of Gustav Mie, University of Freiburg, to introduce modern physics. This was a normal post, though I left in 1933 with the outbreak of the Nazis. Compared with now, clearly, the number of theoretical physicists was minute, and personal relations played an important role.

CHAPTER TWELVE

PHYSICS IN A MINOR DEPARTMENT: 1927–36

H Lipson

Undergraduate Work

I became a student in Liverpool University in 1927. I knew that the physics department was not a distinguished one, and I was told that they rarely awarded first-class Honours, but I had no choice. It was the nearest to my home and since I had scholarships amounting to only about £100 per annum I could not afford to live in any other university town. With fees of £40 and travelling expenses of £20, I could only just afford Liverpool.

The Head of the Department, Professor Wilberforce, regarded himself primarily as a teacher. Like so many professors of physics in those days, he was really a mathematician; physics was regarded as a subject that could easily be picked up by oneself, whereas mathematics was a proper discipline! Nevertheless, he took his duties very seriously and did not succumb to the temptation to make his subject mathematical; he wanted his students to think like physicists. In fact he introduced very little mathematics into his lectures. On one occasion he wrote an integral on the board and the students cheered; he looked very hurt.

He devised some very pretty ways of solving standard problems. I particularly remember his way of tackling the spherical condenser; we did not know what he was trying to do until he came to the end. We were, I am afraid, left with a collection of pretty ideas, but no general ones for tackling new problems. We did not respond well to his methods, and at the end of our first examination he told us that we were the worst year that he had ever had.

He was particularly interested in precession and had some very good lecture demonstrations. For example, he had a gyroscope mounted on stilts which would fall over when the plane of the wheel moved to be at right angles to the plane of the stilts; to prevent this one had to apply a small force to the axis with a paintbrush. Only he could manage this since one's instincts made one apply the force the wrong way. But he never told us of the mathematical relationship between the angular rotation, the moment of inertia, the precession and the applied couple. (I still think that this subject is not given enough emphasis in physics courses.)

At the end of the second year we took a sessional examination and on the basis of this we were chosen to read for Honours; those not chosen would repeat the year and would be awarded ordinary degrees. Only a few—usually two or three—were so chosen, but our year was exceptional; there were eight of us! This was the second largest group that there had ever been; the largest was 13. These numbers make me suspicious of the present-day assertion that only large departments are viable. I think that a variety of departments is necessary, as some students need a lot of competition, whereas others, such as I, flourish with more intimate contact. I can remember the thrill that I experienced when Professor Wilberforce acknowledged me as we crossed in the quad. He knew me!

Our department was unusual in that it had two professors—experimental and theoretical. We did not meet the latter, Professor Rice, until our third year. He was an expert on relativity, which was in those days one of the key subjects in the mind of the general public. He gave popular lectures on the subject; these were very well attended, but left the audience still confused. His lectures to the third year were, fortunately, not confined to relativity; I would not have graduated if an *understanding* of relativity had been required. I knew how to use the equations, which I think is what most students mean when they say that they understand it. He introduced us to quantum theory and I still remember one of his points. Why is there less energy in the high-frequency part of the incandescent spectrum, when the high-frequency quanta are the largest? Well, Rolls-Royces cost more than Fords, but much more money is spent on Fords than on Rolls-Royces. He also introduced us to vector and scalar products. I did not properly get the hang of these until I myself had to introduce students to them. The real way to understand any topic is to have to teach it to others.

Lecturing

Lecturing has not changed greatly since I was a student. Certainly there have been many new ideas, but I do not think that they have been fundamental. Some people maintain that a student should be given duplicated notes of a lecture so that he should be able to concentrate upon what the lecturer is saying, instead of having to write at the same time. I disagree. I found that the taking of one's own notes is essential to understanding. Sometimes I would leave a lecture with no clear idea of what had been said, but the disentangling of my rough notes clarified the lecture for me. But we must leave students free time for this process of digestion.

There is no way of defining the perfect lecturer, in spite of what students seem to think. We had two mathematics lecturers, both very good and quite different from each other. The applied maths man was very formal and would dictate his lecture at dictation speed, so that I could leave his lecture with a complete record. The pure maths man was informal, and I had to go over his notes myself. I found both of them very helpful. We were given plenty of examples to do for ourselves. We were given Fourier analysis to carry out and resynthesise, to prove that we had the right answer; this stood me in good stead in my research later. I gather that students do not have such work now. I think that this is a pity.

I remember one incident, however, which left me aggrieved. The applied maths man had set us a problem on maximising the trajectory of a body propelled from a finite height above a plane. After a great deal of effort I managed to solve it—the only one in a class of about thirty. I gained a *very* small tick and the comment 'Too long'! But the main fact that I learnt from these mathematicians was that I would never make a mathematician.

Research

We confounded Professor Wilberforce by turning out to be the *best* year he had ever had: four out of the eight of us gained first-class Honours degrees. This created a problem; two of us wanted to do research in the department and only one member of staff wanted an assistant. So we tossed up for it. And I lost! My friend went on to do research in the mechanical properties of metal single crystals and I was allotted to help another research student—C A Beevers—who had graduated a year earlier. Losing the toss turned out to be the most fortunate thing that has happened to me during my life. The research was on x-ray crystallography, a subject that just suited my semi-numerical mind. I think that I would have been no use in a subject that required meticulous accuracy.

Dr Roberts, the only really serious research worker in the department, had decided that the department ought to diversify and so chose crystal-structure determination. An earlier student had started, had built himself a demountable x-ray tube, had been put to work on a rather precious mineral and had lost it! Arnold Beevers had spent a year on getting the x-ray tube to work and had learnt to take and to interpret oscillation photographs, but that was all. We had no supervisor and no idea what crystals were worth looking at. I chose an orthorhombic crystal—potassium hydrogen tartrate—but could get nowhere with understanding the diffraction patterns. In 1930 very few crystal structures were known and some—even those published in the *Proceedings of the Royal Society*—were clearly wrong. There was little literature to go on. Bernal had devised ways of interpreting oscillation photographs, Astbury and Yardley (later Lonsdale) had published a standard work on space groups, there was the Braggs' book on *X-rays and Crystal Structure* and Wyckoff had summarised published work. It was, therefore, not difficult to cover the literature on this new subject. But how to do something fresh?

We transferred our attention to a tetragonal crystal, $BeSO_4 \cdot 4H_2O$, whose published structure was clearly nonsense (it had flat SO_4 groups!) but we couldn't see how to put it right: so we plucked up our courage and visited W L Bragg's laboratory in Manchester, 40 miles away. And there, thanks particularly to W H Taylor, we managed to get on the right lines. In particular, we found that not everything that appears in print must be right! This, to present-day research students, may sound rather tough—no supervision, almost insoluble problems, few facilities and little money. But I now know that it was very good training for us. We had to think for ourselves and to envisage new concepts.

Beevers and I both took MSc degrees after one year's research. We did not, however, go on to take a PhD; our professor did not believe in this new-fangled idea, the sequence BSc, MSc, and DSc was good enough without the unnatural intrusion of PhD. It is not now realised how much resistance there was to this new degree. One professor here called it the 'fiddle-de-dee'! I understand that here Rutherford was its main champion, on the grounds that if we in this country did not provide research students with the opportunity of gaining a Doctorate, they would go to other countries where they did. This was certainly not true for Rutherford's department, but it may have been so for others less distinguished.

Research Apparatus

The apparatus that we used for research provided perhaps the greatest contrast with the present day. We were past—but only just past—the days of string and sealing-wax, but we had to make most of the devices that we wanted. Our AC was provided by an alternator in the basement (there was no other AC in the building) and we could not use it on the one day that our professor gave his lecture on AC. We had pumps and one HT transformer, but that was all.

We had, as I have said, a home-made gas x-ray tube, pumped out by a system consisting of a rotary oil pump and a Gaede rotary mercury pump. This latter was similar in action to a rotary oil pump, but it used two litres of mercury and was very slow; it would take a whole day to get down to x-ray vacuum (of the order of 10^{-3} mm Hg). When we wanted x-rays we had to start the day before and put a note on the apparatus to say that it should not be switched off at night. To keep the pressure right we had a very crude leak that had to be continually corrected. We were not happy with this and decided to make ourselves a hot-filament tube—then known as a Coolidge tube. This meant having to learn workshop techniques, with a lathe and a drilling machine. Unfortunately, I had picked up soldering methods from my father, who used to put his soldering iron in the fire and wait until it was red-hot. I now know why his soldering was so unsatisfactory. (When I asked my family to buy me an electric soldering iron for my birthday, they thought that I was mad; but they gave it to me and I still have it and occasionally use it.)

Our Coolidge tube had as an insulator a safety-lamp glass, sealed to the metal ends with sealing wax. We made our own filaments. We could now follow the pumping by observing the striations as the pressure fell, becoming further and further spaced until they finally disappeared and we knew that we were there. But it was all very slow. So, once again, we plucked up courage and asked our professor for permission to buy a new-fangled device—a mercury diffusion pump. This was rather expensive (about £8, I think) but he agreed, and we fixed it to our Coolidge tube. It required 50 cc of mercury (not two litres) and was heated by a Bunsen burner. We lit the burner and waited, watching the discharge. It took a few minutes to heat up and then, in a flash, the discharge swept out of the tube. It was one of the greatest moments in my research life!

Now we had a really controllable tube and this made life much easier. We were not really happy, however, with only photographic methods, and decided to build ourselves an ionisation spectrometer, copying the one that we had used in Manchester. But this proved to be too ambitious, and we had to abandon this idea. In any case, we found that we did not need great accuracy for our work; eye estimations of intensity were good enough for all that we wanted to do.

Research Results

At first we used only standard methods to work out crystal structures, if anything could be called standard at that time. (The discipline was only about 15 years old, if one discounts the war years, 1914–18). By 1934 we had worked out two tetragonal crystal structures, but we thought that it would be good for our experience if we tried a different system. After some intense discussion (during which I cut myself badly with a broken bottle and had to dash off to hospital) we chose blue vitriol, $CuSO_4 \cdot 5H_2O$, a common chemical in laboratories. This was triclinic, its unit cell being a general parallelepiped. This was too difficult. By a stroke of luck we were able to recognise relationships between the intensities of the diffraction spots that gave us the positions of the copper and sulphur atoms, but model-building gave us no clues about possible positions of the oxygen atoms and the water molecules; five was an odd number to fit in.

Beevers then said to me 'What about trying the Fourier method that Bragg has recently advocated?' We went over to Manchester again and were allowed to use the ionisation spectrometer there. (We are still proud of having used this very idiosyncratic instrument.) But we had no idea how to sum a two-dimensional Fourier series. One-dimensional series with a few terms was all right, but two-dimensional series with 90 terms was another matter. Still, we devised a method that took us about a month of mental arithmetic and it worked! That is, it gave us an interpretable result. This was the first structure of any complexity that had been derived by this method. The peaks were not nice and round, as they should have been, but they were good enough. There was, however, one small peak that we could not account for; we called it a 'ghost'. When we showed our Fourier synthesis to Professor Wilberforce and pointed the ghost out to him, he called it the 'spectre in the spectra'. (He was known as the jester of the University.) Professor Bragg was also delighted.

The synthesis was summed by makeshift methods, in which one of us read numbers off a long strip at regular intervals dependent upon one index; the other wrote them down in a prepared table. We then added the columns. It occurred to us that the line of numbers might come in useful again, and so we wrote them on a card which we filed. In this way, the Beevers–Lipson strips arose. These strips excited some interest, and several people asked to be allowed to copy them. We spent some time discussing with Professor Bragg and others the possibility of printing them, but the cost was very great—around £200. In the end Manchester University lent us the money (we were then both in Manchester) and by selling the strips we were soon able to repay the money and even make a profit. So, without even intending to, or even realising what was happening, we became famous! The strips became standard and from then on all crystal-structure determination used Fourier methods, mainly using our strips for summation.

Publication of Results

The department at Liverpool did not produce many published papers, roughly one every other year. We published our first paper, with advice and help from Professor Bragg, in 1932. Then it became a flood. In each of two successive years, 1934 and 1935, we published four papers. I gather that this created much comment in the Senior Common Room—to which we did not belong—because the University published each year a summary of published papers from all departments. The papers, of course, did overlap somewhat. It was usual to have a preliminary letter in *Nature*, to establish priority, the full structure being published later. Priority was important. After we had published one structure, Wyckoff—one of the important names in the subject—reported that he had also worked out the structure and his result agreed substantially with ours. We were glad that we had got in first!

Professor Bragg was extremely helpful, both in advising on the form of papers and in getting them accepted. But on one occasion we did not take his advice. When we wanted to publish one on the strip method, he said that too many papers were being published and couldn't we incorporate it in our paper on copper sulphate? We were able to evade his advice because he had to go abroad. The paper was published, in *Philosophical Magazine*, in a few weeks. Apparently the referee realised its importance. We still think that our decision was right. If we had taken Bragg's advice, there would have been one paper less, but the volume of content would have been the same, and the method might have been overlooked.

Summary

I hope that this chapter has given some idea of what it was like to be an undergraduate and a research student in the 1930s. I was not, of course, typical—no one is. We had an unpromising start, being in a department not noted for research, but we were so keen on getting results that this did not matter. But I do not claim that our success was achieved by persistence; Beevers was lively, but I was very retiring. I am to this day grateful to him, and to my mother, for bringing me out of my shell. We were, of course, lucky to be so close to the world centre of research in our subject (it did not, in fact, seem so to a couple of impecunious young men) and that Professor Bragg was so helpful. I claim that never was the losing of the toss of a coin so fortunate!

CHAPTER THIRTEEN

TEACHING AND RESEARCH IN THE CAVENDISH: 1929–35

D Shoenberg

I entered Trinity College, Cambridge, as a maths scholar in 1929. Although my father was keen that I should eventually become a physicist, my private ambition was to continue in mathematics. At Trinity it was then the practice for maths scholars to be thrown in at the deep end. It was assumed that they were already familiar with all the first year work and they were sent straightaway to second year lectures. For me this was rather a quantum leap and although I found some of the new ideas exciting they were mostly over my head, and by the end of my first year I was sufficiently discouraged to abandon my private ambition and to agree to switch to physics.

From my point of view the great advantage of approaching physics by coming to it after a first year of maths was that I could concentrate on physics alone for the remaining two years and avoid having to do any chemistry, which I had not studied seriously since 'Matric' (the then equivalent of O level). Indeed, in order to get a maths scholarship I had paid little attention at school to physics either and the switch to physics in my second undergraduate year proved a bit like jumping out of the frying pan into the fire. The trouble was that I lacked the kind of intuitive and descriptive approach familiar to those who had concentrated on science at school and, even though I could cope with the bits of rather simple mathematical analysis that came in here and there, I often found it difficult to relate them to any kind of physical reality. Thus the formal treatment of thermodynamics which I had from A H Wilson's lectures in the maths faculty appealed to me more than that of Thirkill's course on heat and elementary thermodynamics for first year science students. I could usually solve the problems set after each of Wilson's lectures but I had little idea of the 'physical' meaning of the solutions.

In 1930 the new quantum mechanics was already something like four years old but little of it appeared in the physics teaching, though it was already being taught as an advanced topic in the maths faculty. At the beginning of my third year I went to A H Wilson's lectures on the quantum theory of spectra and once again I could cope with the mathematical analysis which was very clearly presented, and could work through even fairly difficult problems such as an approximate calculation by the variational principle of the energy levels of the helium atom, but I had little real feeling for what it all meant. However, the isolation of theoretical physics within the mathematics faculty was beginning to break down about then. This I think came about through the influence of R H Fowler who was Rutherford's son-in-law and the doyen of the theoretical community. Although Fowler's research students and associates had no official footing in the Cavendish (they usually worked in their own rooms or the library), they did attend colloquia and eventually one of them, N F Mott, gave regular lectures on wave mechanics in the Cavendish. This course was meant to convey the basic physical ideas without using any elaborate mathematics and my recollection is that I made less of it than I did of Wilson's more formal treatment—this in spite of Mott's efforts to put the trickier points across by suddenly beaming at the audience in his characteristic way.

Fowler himself gave a regular course in the maths faculty on the methods of mathematical physics and though some of it was well over my head in my first undergraduate year, it did provide me with a valuable grounding in some important techniques, such as vector analysis. I think it was in this course that I was first introduced to the pitfalls of statistics by an ingenious argument. Fowler asked everyone in the audience to say how many children there were in his family. He then took the arithmetic mean of all the answers and asked if this would be a reasonable estimate of the average number of children per family in the country. Most of us thought it should be, apart from possible fluctuations, but Fowler rather triumphantly pointed out that the estimate failed to take account of families with no children and so must inevitably be exaggerated!

As time went on I developed an enthusiasm for physics and gradually began to get a feeling for what it was all about. I think an important factor in creating this interest and understanding was that Rutherford's Cavendish was just then passing through an exciting time, culminating in Cockcroft and Walton's first disintegration of nuclei by artificially accelerated protons, Chadwick's discovery of the neutron and Blackett's confirmation of the discovery of the positron, all in 1932, my final undergraduate year. It was an inspiration to be taught by the very people who were making the discoveries and who had themselves been inspired by Rutherford's simple and direct approach to physics.

Rutherford himself was not at his best in his lectures to undergraduates on the constitution of matter. I had the impression that he regarded these lectures as a somewhat boring duty. This opinion, however, may not be altogether fair, for I went to this course in my first year, when I had perhaps too little background to appreciate it. Rutherford really came into his own when at the beginning of each academic year he gave the opening lecture of the Cavendish Physical Society. He would then review with real enthusiasm what had happened in the Cavendish during the past year and what he intended should happen next. It was easy to get the chauvinistic impression that this was the only physics that mattered and indeed at the time, perhaps it was still nearly true.

Blackett's lectures on optics were something of a revelation in showing me how Kirchhoff's theory provided a real basis for diffraction theory. Previously I had been baffled by the more elementary treatment, for I could not see why it was taken for granted that each point on a wavefront could be regarded as a secondary source. I also went in my final year to a course Blackett gave on properties of matter, which included all sorts of topics which couldn't be easily fitted in elsewhere, for instance as the theory of errors. This was in fact a repetition of a course given the previous year by E G Dymond who had left for a post in Edinburgh. By my final year I was better able to take in the meaning of the material and I was captivated by Blackett's enthusiastic style of presentation and his frankness in admitting occasionally that he himself didn't fully understand a particular point. One example that sticks in my memory was a formula he wrote down for the probable errors of the values of the coefficients in a linear regression determined by the least squares method. He told us he had found the formula in a reference book but he didn't know how to derive it. I was rather keen on statistical matters and after brooding about the problem for some time I suddenly saw how to solve it while I was watching a film at the cinema and was very flattered to be complimented by Blackett when I showed him my solution.

Other lectures in the Cavendish which I particularly remember as being interesting and valuable in their various ways were those by Ratcliffe on topics connected with wireless, Cockcroft on electrodynamics and Kapitza on magnetism. Ratcliffe was in charge of a small group researching on the ionosphere—one of the few topics in the Cavendish not dominated by Rutherford. His lectures were a model of lucid presentation, delivered at just the right pace for easy absorption and he avoided putting in too many qualifications and complications which could confuse someone new to the subject. For me they were particularly interesting because my father had been associated with the Marconi Company since the very early years of wireless. But although I had grown up with wireless almost in my blood, I had never really understood how it worked and it was very satisfying to discover that it was after all rather simple and not the holy mystery I had found it till then.

Cockcroft's lectures on electrodynamics, though delivered in a more pedestrian and deadpan style, were a valuable supplement to Ratcliffe's in providing the more formal mathematical treatment of the basic theory.

Kapitza was somewhat of a legend in Cambridge, for his ingenious and original pioneer work on very high magnetic fields, for his eccentricities and for his unusual status as an important figure in the Cambridge scientific establishment while still remaining a Soviet subject. He gave an advanced course of lectures once a week in the Lent term on recent researches in magnetism—much of it on his own work—which I found both interesting and entertaining. But it was sometimes difficult to follow, partly because of his strong Russian accent, his rather high pitched voice and his peculiar English constructions and partly because he was careless and untidy in what he wrote on the blackboard. I remember one occasion when at the end of the lecture I asked him to resolve a contradiction in the notes I had taken and he replied 'If I make everything so clear that there are no contradictions there is nothing left for you to think about and you won't learn anything.' This possibility of consulting the lecturer about what he had said was a valuable advantage of the relatively small classes in those days. There were typically only 20 or 30 students in the final physics year, rather than the 100 or so today, so that it was easier to establish some degree of personal relationship between students and staff.

Two other features of the Cambridge system which also contributed to the establishment of such informal contacts were the practical classes and college supervisions. These features are, of course, still there today but perhaps less effective than they used to be because of the increased numbers. A valuable lesson I learnt from the practical classes was the importance of interpreting unexpected departures from the ideal behaviour described in the book of words. It is always tempting to attribute such apparent anomalies to gremlins, but careful study of the data may sometimes reveal significant underlying aspects of the experiment and may even lead to the discovery of something quite new. In the advanced practical class run by Blackett and Dee there was a lot of emphasis on the do-it-yourself approach and making the most of rather simple apparatus of the string and sealing-wax variety. Blackett was rather a virtuoso both in optimising the design of an experiment and in analysing the resulting data to get the most out of it. He was at that time developing an automatic cloud chamber to record cosmic ray tracks—one of the early developments which took the Cavendish from string and sealing-wax into the machine age—and would talk to us enthusiastically about the subtleties of design involved. It was not long afterwards that he photographed the positron tracks with this equipment.

College supervisions were rather hit or miss affairs. Sometimes I was unsuccessful in getting the supervisor to appreciate at what a low level my difficulties lay, but on other occasions I was inspired by the enthusiasm with which the supervisor would tell me about his own research. C D Ellis was a very clear expositor and loved to talk about the intricacies of β-ray spectra which he had done so much himself to unravel. N A de Bruyne—a keen amateur airman—had recently worked on radio valves at GEC and gave the impression that physics was mostly concerned with thermionic emission. From Ellis I also learnt the art of how to present a piece of physics clearly by first setting out the basic observations in a rational order and then giving a logically argued interpretation. This teaching stood me in good stead not only when writing examination answers but ever since in my scientific writing.

In the final examination there was a large choice of questions (see appendix to this Chapter for an example) and I was lucky in being able to avoid most of the topics involving classical physics of the kind I had not properly absorbed. Instead I was able to show off some familiarity with recent ideas involving wave mechanics and with the more mathematical aspects of thermodynamics and electrodynamics. Indeed I had more luck than I deserved in that the questions included an undue proportion of topics which I had particularly revised just before the examination, such as the quantum mechanical interpretation of α-ray spectra which had only recently appeared in Gamow's textbook.

I was lucky again in the practical examination. The problem was to determine the exponent in Steimetz's law which relates the energy loss in a hysteresis cycle to a power of the maximum value of B in the cycle; the method was based on the deflections of a ballistic galvanometer when the field was suddenly changed. Most of the candidates were fooled by the presence of a reversing switch among the items of apparatus provided and I could see that they were very soon busy recording deflections as they reversed the current giving the exciting field. I was sorely puzzled because I couldn't see how a hysteresis loop could be plotted in this way. So, quite early in the day, I decided to confess my bafflement to the invigilator and ask for help. The point that I (and everyone else) had missed was that the field could be changed in small steps by pulling out plugs in a series resistance box and the reversing switch was only needed for changing the sense of the field once it had got down to zero. I was then able to go ahead and at the end of the day had got enough data together to make a logarithmic plot which gave the exponent as 1.6 (by a fluke exactly the textbook answer, as I later discovered). No doubt I was penalised for the help I got, but I was the only one who completed the experiment; many of the others also eventually asked for help but too late to make full use of it. Another useful lesson: never be too proud to confess your ignorance!

Perhaps as a result of all this luck I managed to get a First, which qualified me to continue as a graduate student (in those days we were called research students). In choosing a field of research I deviated from the usual rule of going into nuclear physics. Rather naïvely, but perhaps understandably seeing that 1932 was the *annus mirabilis* of nuclear physics, I felt that all the great discoveries had already been made, and indeed the emphasis in nuclear physics was beginning to be on more sophisticated measurements using elaborate electronics (of which I was rather ignorant). At the same time, in the courtyard of the Cavendish there was a beautiful new building going up for Kapitza to expand his pioneer work on high magnetic fields and low temperatures. As I have already said, Kapitza was a rather exotic figure and his subject, then just beginning to be called solid state physics, seemed, perhaps because of the way he gave his lectures, particularly mysterious and attractive. Even though much of Kapitza's own work involved elaborate engineering, there was still room in his field for the string and sealing-wax kind of experiment I could handle and I felt it would be easier to do something really new there, rather than in nuclear physics. So in the autumn of 1932 I started work in the Royal Society Mond Laboratory, which was officially opened soon afterwards with great éclat by Stanley Baldwin, the then Chancellor of the University.

However, I had first to undergo the traditional introduction to research in the Cavendish, which was a few weeks of practical work in the summer on vacuum technique under Chadwick's supervision. The equipment provided was rather primitive—only a hand-operated Fleuss pump and a home-made diffusion pump—and the work consisted mainly of chasing leaks in poorly constructed glassware. It was a very hot summer and it was easy to get discouraged, but Chadwick would come by occasionally and encourage us with some gloomily sympathetic remark. He had made glass joints with a candle flame when he was interned in Ruhleben during World War I and felt we were lucky to have gas.

Although Kapitza's new Mond Laboratory was in a separate building it was really still part of the Cavendish, so that I saw a good deal of what was going on more directly under Rutherford. In spite of the gradual changeover from string and sealing-wax to modern technology, as in Cockcroft and Walton's disintegration work as well as Kapitza's and Blackett's researches, much of the old atmosphere was still there. The administration was practically non-existent—just the Professor's secretary (a rather gruff man called Hayles who was also Rutherford's lecture assistant). I think it was Kapitza who started a revolution by employing a girl for the first time. She was Miss Stebbings who, after Kapitza's return to Russia, succeeded Hayles as Rutherford's secretary and did everything from book-keeping to running the library. I don't think the administration was any less efficient then than it is now with something like 10 or 20 times as many administrative staff—though of course the number of scientific workers and students has increased four-fold and the growing support of science by the State has enormously increased the bureaucratic load.

Figure 13.1 Miss Stebbings succeeded Hayles as Rutherford's secretary in the 1930s.

For the research students an important figure in the laboratory was Fred Lincoln, the laboratory steward, who jealously guarded the stores and was famous for his thriftiness. It was only very reluctantly that he would give out a few feet of wire and he would usually prefer to search the scrap box rather than give out anything new. The students were rather terrified of him and were afraid of approaching him unless they really had to. I remember one of my friends, who was trying to separate the isotopes of lithium, wasted nearly a year because he did not dare to ask Lincoln for a fresh supply of metal and it turned out in the end that Lincoln had made a mistake and had given him sodium instead of lithium. My own relations with Lincoln were quite friendly since the Mond had its own stores and I needed to turn to him only in a real emergency. Another important character was Felix Niedergesass the glass-blower, who like all glass-blowers was a little mysterious and boastful about his craft, but was very helpful to the students and would give private lessons in glass-blowing at his home close to the Cavendish.

The Cavendish in those days was small enough for all of us to get to know each other, even though working in quite different fields. Such

Figure 13.2   Fred Lincoln, an important figure for the students in
the Laboratory.

Figure 13.3   Felix Niedergesass the glass-blower.

contacts were facilitated by meeting at tea every day (though on special occasions the Mond had its own separate tea with Mrs Kapitza presiding at the samovar) and at various seminars and colloquia. The most prestigious of these was the Cavendish Physical Society with formal lectures by well-known physicists, while the Cavendish Colloquium provided an opportunity for research students to report on their own work. There were also informal meetings outside the laboratory of bodies such as the $\nabla^2 V$ Club and the Kapitza Club. There was no formal program of graduate lectures but there were all sorts of opportunities to follow up special interests by attending advanced lectures of various kinds. I remember particularly Dirac's lectures on quantum mechanics, which followed very closely the textbook he had just published, and Wishart's lectures on statistics, both in the maths faculty, and Wooster's lectures on crystallography in the mineralogy department.

Rutherford presided over the Cavendish rather like the genial (but occasionally wrathful) father of a family. Even though I was working outside his own field, he had always taken a great interest in Kapitza's work and supported it generously in all sorts of ways. He would from time to time walk round the laboratory and ask how everyone was getting on. There was usually some warning of such a visit because you could hear his voice booming loudly when he was still a few rooms away and this gave you a chance to collect your wits. The people who worked with Geiger counters, which were rather sensitive to noise, had an illuminated sign 'Talk softly' which looked as if it was specially meant for Rutherford. There is also an apocryphal story that Kaptiza's nickname of 'crocodile' for Rutherford was after the crocodile in Peter Pan, which had to swallow an alarm-clock in order that the children should not be frightened, for they would hear it coming before they saw it. Kapitza was certainly fond of the crocodile symbol and had Eric Gill carve a life-size bas-relief of a crocodile by the front door of the Mond; this was revealed during the formal opening which Baldwin performed with a gilded key in the shape of a crocodile.

Research supervision then as now varied considerably between one supervisor and another. I found Kapitza's style stimulating; he would drop in for a chat about progress fairly frequently and it was always possible to appeal for help when you were stuck. I was trying to develop a method of measuring the feeble magnetostriction of bismuth crystals in the field of an ordinary electromagnet. The expected changes of length were very small, only of the order of 10^{-7} cm, and I often despaired of reaching the required sensitivity. Kapitza, however, loved a challenge and when consulted would quickly make a whole lot of ingenious suggestions. Each suggestion by itself might only bring a factor of 2 improvement, but with six such suggestions the improvement should have been 2^6 and with a further two even more clever sugges-

Figure 13.4 Assistant staff at the Cavendish Laboratory, 1929. Front row: (left to right) Roff, Everett, Lincoln, Rolph, Hayles. Middle row: Linsey, Crowe, Simpson, Dear, Morley, Thompson, Aves. Last row: Chapman, Lauremann, Pearson, Dean, Tilly, Nutt. (Courtesy of the Cavendish Laboratory, Cambridge.)

tions, each of which might bring a factor 3, it looked as if my difficulties were over, since the improvement should have been by a factor of nearly 600 and 100 or so was all that was needed. But when I started putting his suggestions into practice I would find that the factors of 2 might in reality be only 1.2 and the factors 3 only 1.5, so the overall improvement factor was only 6 rather than 600. However I was that much nearer my goal and ready for Kapitza's next visit with a new batch of suggestions.

My supervision by Kapitza ended somewhat dramatically in 1934 when he was not allowed to return to Cambridge from a summer visit to the Soviet Union. Once it was clear that Kapitza would not return, Rutherford became official head of the Mond, though unofficially Cockcroft deputised for him a good deal; Rutherford also took over my supervision. By then I had completed the magnetostriction problem and fortunately was able to think of new problems on my own, but Rutherford took his supervision seriously and now included me in his regular round of visits. He would be particularly interested if there were some results to report and he had an almost uncanny way of getting straight to the heart of the matter. Even though he knew relatively little about the background of the work I was doing (mainly studies of the magnetic susceptibility of bismuth) he had a knack of seeing immediately just what was missing in what I told him and asking 'Why didn't you measure that?' or 'What are you going to get out of this—just give me a general idea?'

My examiners for the PhD were Rutherford and Cockcroft and I still remember some of Rutherford's questions which helped to put me at ease in the oral examination. In my dissertation there was a good deal about k-vectors and k-space in connection with the theory of metals, but I had never really explained what k meant and Rutherford asked: 'Now just tell me, in simple language, what is this k you keep talking about?' One of his other questions was I believe also typical: 'How would you measure the magnetic field of the sun and how big is it?' I was greatly relieved to find that he was quite happy with my vague answer that it might be possible to look at the Zeeman effect and, if this was the method, presumably the field must be a few thousand gauss.

The PhD marks the end of a student's career as a student so this is perhaps an appropriate place to finish this rather rambling account of what it was like in the good old days so long ago. My account has been perhaps too egocentric and my memories may not always be reliable but I hope I have conveyed something of the atmosphere of those days and of the contrasts and similarities compared with what it is like today.

Appendix 13A: A specimen paper from 1932, indicating the questions attempted

NATURAL SCIENCES TRIPOS. PART II.

SATURDAY, *May* 28, 1932.   1.30—4.30.

PHYSICS. (4)

Three *questions only should be attempted.*

22. Discuss the theory of the α-particle type of radioactive disintegration.

Or

Give an account of the experimental methods used in studying the artificial disintegration of the elements and indicate the general results which have been obtained.

23. Discuss critically the methods which have been used to measure e/m_0. Explain the importance of an accurate knowledge of this constant.

24. Develop the electron theory of dielectric media. How far does the theory account for the relation between dielectric constant and density?

25. Summarise our experimental knowledge of the dispersion of light and give a theory to account for the results. Describe briefly the effect of an imposed magnetic field.

26. Give a general account of the electrical condition of the atmosphere. What agencies have been suggested as possible causes of this electrification?

27. Give an account of the experimental evidence on the diffraction of material waves.

Hydrogen molecules are allowed to escape from a box at room temperature through a narrow slit and to impinge on the cleavage plane of a crystal. Shew that for grazing incidence specular reflection may be expected.

$$N = 6 \cdot 06 \times 10^{23}; \quad h = 6 \cdot 55 \times 10^{-27} \text{ erg sec.}$$

28. Discuss the evidence that no two electrons in an atom can be in the same quantum state, referring in this connection to X-ray spectra and the periodic table of elements.

CHAPTER FOURTEEN

OXFORD PHYSICS IN TRANSITION: 1929–39

R V Jones

At the time when I went up to Oxford in 1929, competition for scholarships and their minor counterparts, exhibitions, was severe: typically there were about ten competitors for any one award, although a candidate could enter for two or even three competitions in a year. Most prospective physicists aimed for entry to Cambridge rather than Oxford, because of the former's enormous prestige; but in my own case I had excluded the alternative because of a partisan loyalty to Oxford in the boat race as a schoolboy. In fact, if I had pursued my original intention to become a chemist, Oxford would have been the better choice because of the high standing of Oxford chemistry; but in my last years at school I had come to appreciate physics as the more fundamental subject, thanks largely to good schoolteaching and to broadcast talks by Oliver Lodge and James Jeans. So when I was awarded an exhibition to Wadham College, I decided to read physics rather than chemistry—a decision that was welcomed by the sole Fellow of the College in science, T C Keeley, who became my tutor.

Keeley recommended me to read Honour Moderations in Mathematics for the first year. This was a strain because it involved doing nothing but mathematics in a course that had no regard to the interests of prospective physicists. The Mathematics School was dominated by G H Hardy, who openly took pride in the fact that his kind of mathematics was unlikely to be turned to useful purposes. One distinguished graduate of the School, the late O G Sutton (Director of the Meteorological Office) commented that Hardy's attitude had ruined the School. Courses that I can vaguely recall included analysis, determinants and matrices, projective geometry, differential equations and dynamics, which were all taught abstractly. I even ventured into some hydrodynamics lectures given by J W Nicholson in Balliol, who amazed us by smoking in academic dress, and by removing his false teeth and placing them on the lectern beside him while he lectured because he said they hurt. The story among the five of us who made up his audience was that some twenty years before he had been anticipated by Bohr in formulating the quantum theory of the atom, and had ever since drowned his disappointment in the well-stocked cellars of Balliol. Later I found there was substance to both the physical and the bibulatory aspects of the story.

At the beginning of the second year I moved into physics and gradually came to learn the history of the subject in Oxford over the past century. The principal laboratory was the Clarendon, so-called because it had been built with funds originally raised from the sale of the Clarendon State Papers with the intention of financing a riding school. Fortunately it took from 1751 to 1860 for the funds to accumulate sufficiently, and the Trustees then decided that Oxford would benefit more from physics than from horsemanship. They thus to some extent compensated the academic world for its loss when in 1830 the clairvoyant citizens of Dumfries, having been left a benefaction with which to found a university, built a lunatic asylum instead.

The Clarendon Laboratory was opened in 1870; R B Clifton, who had been elected to the Royal Society in 1868, was appointed Professor of Experimental Philosophy in 1865 and became head of the laboratory. Clifton was evidently a young man of promise, but the legend in my time was that one of the earliest papers which he had published after taking up the Chair was shown to be sadly in error, and from that point onwards he eschewed research in favour of teaching. As a result the Clarendon was moribund until Lindemann's appointment 50 years later.

In the meantime there had been an attempt to improve physics in Oxford by the creation of a second chair, the Wykeham Chair of Physics, and the building of a new laboratory, the Electrical Laboratory. J S E Townsend, who had been with J J Thomson in Cambridge and who may not have received due credit for his share in the discoveries in the Cavendish, was appointed to the Wykeham Chair. Townsend was thus well established in post when F A Lindemann arrived in 1919 as the Professor of Experimental Philosophy to revitalise the Clarendon. In my time feelings between the two laboratories were so strained that when the staff in the Clarendon heard that those in the Electrical Laboratory were going to give a lecture course in high vacua, they talked of putting on a rival course entitled 'higher vacua'.

Townsend frequently questioned the validity of the quantum theory, his *bêtes noires* being the experiments of Franck and Hertz, and those of Ramsauer, about which he wrote papers in refutation. Lindemann happily told a story of Townsend's two sons quarrelling in the University Parks and hurling insults at one another: 'You're a Franck' said one, 'And you're Hertz' said the other. 'That's nothing' replied the first,

'You're a J J!' In such an atmosphere a coherent course of physics was unlikely to evolve. This was perhaps of less importance in Oxford than it would have been elsewhere because lectures were not regarded as a particularly important channel of instruction. Attendance was not compulsory and some of the lectures seemed to be given more for the *amour propre* of the lecturer, or for compliance with statutory obligations, than for any zeal to teach. Their quality was widely uneven. At one extreme were those given by one delightful man whose diction was nearly unintelligible, as was his writing on the blackboard on those occasions when we could see it before his body obscured it as he rubbed it out with his left hand almost as soon as he had written it with his right. At the other extreme were those of G M B Dobson on meteorology, which were models of clarity and interest. Those of Lindemann came somewhere in-between: lucid in expression but hardly audible beyond the third row. Typically there would be two lectures to attend each morning, including Saturday, and on some days another at 5 PM. Afternoons were usually vacant for sport, or for work in the library as Finals approached.

Practical work in laboratories averaged around two hours each day, although some of us would put in more. Experiments ranged from the simple to the complex, occasionally involving such advanced techniques as making mirror surfaces by spattering or evaporation, but more often determining such properties as surface tension by several different methods. We were all expected to learn to blow glass to the extent of making T-pieces. No great regard was paid to safety; for example in the handling of radioactive sources. I was all but electrocuted by a double-pole, double-throw knife switch with unguarded terminals with which my large hands could barely avoid contact in switching in a 600 volt generator.

The work turned some of us into skilled experimenters: but not all—there was an Ensign from the U S Navy on a Rhodes Scholarship in my year who failed Finals completely. He stayed for an extra year for a second attempt, when he did little better: however, the examiners felt that they ought to give him every chance of a degree, and when he said that he did not know how to tackle the last practical examination they offered him the chance of doing any experiment that he cared to choose. When he said he could not think of any, the examiners suggested that he should determine the density of a penny using Archimedes' principle. He at once asked how he should proceed and was told to weigh the coin in air and then in water and determine the density from the difference. He went off, only to return reproachfully an hour or more later and said that he had found that the coin weighed just as much in water as in air, which was what any sensible man would expect. Actually, his was a remarkable feat in failure if only because Oxford was unique in having four classes of Honours. (There was no soft nonsense about II.1s and II.2s, simply I, II, III and IV.) The Chairman of the examiners in my time held that these were awarded as follows: 'The Firsts are for the examiners' friends. The Seconds are for the candidates who are pretty good. The Thirds are for those who are not so good, and the Fourths are for the examiners' friends!'

The priority generally in the Oxford system was not so much given to laboratories or lectures, but to tutorials. A tutor would advise his pupils on which lectures to attend and which books to buy and to read; they would be expected to meet him, often singly, for a regular hour each week and submit for his comments the written work that he had set them in the previous week. This would sometimes be an essay on a subject which he had proposed, but more often my own tutor would expect me to write out answers to a selection of questions taken from previous Honours papers. The depth to which any particular question would be answered was largely left to oneself; in my own case this would sometimes entail writing up to a hundred quarto pages in a week, resorting not only to the wide range of textbooks in the library but also to original papers. The fact that we had to present our work every week to our tutors was a valuable act of discipline. The weakness of the system was that one usually had the same tutor throughout the course of two, or even three, years, and no single tutor could be expected to be well versed in all the branches of physics that would occur in the Honours examinations.

The Honours examination consisted of five three-hour written papers, taken consecutively on Thursday, Friday and Saturday morning, and three six-hour days of practicals on the following Monday, Tuesday and Wednesday. The first three of the written papers were taken by all candidates and were scheduled to include the properties of matter, sound, heat (including thermodynamics), light, electricity and magnetism. The recommended textbooks for these papers were Poynting and Thomson, *Textbooks of Physics*, Preston's *Heat* and *Light*, Barton's *Sound*, Bloch's *Kinetic Theory*, Sackur's *Thermodynamics and Thermochemistry*, Starling's *Electricity and Magnetism* (or Pidduck's *Treatise on Electricity*) and Crowther's *Ions and Ionising Radiations*. While *The Properties of Matter* by Newman and Searle was not specifically recommended, it was the alternative recommended by my tutor, and of all my undergraduate textbooks it has with J K Roberts' *Heat and Thermodynamics* best stood the advance of time. I was similarly recommended Houstoun's *Theory of Light*; although it was full of interest, some of its presentation of mathematics was exasperating and in retrospect I would have preferred R W Wood's *Physical Optics* or Drude's *Optics* which, although it was even then out of date (being pre-quantum theory), is still a mine of interesting points which can rarely be found elsewhere.

Following the three papers which were taken by all candidates there were two others on a specialised subject which, if he wished to attain the highest Honours, the individual candidate had to select from one of three options: advanced electromagnetism or statistical physics or atomic physics. Typically, each of these papers would contain nine questions, and good answers to any four in each paper would be sufficient to qualify for a First Class. This might sound easy, but the advanced nature of the questions offset the seemingly wide choice that they presented. Moreover, the system was so flexible that a deeply thorough answer to as few as two questions, or even one, might still be assessed as a First Class paper. Summary guidance to the syllabus for each of the three subjects was given in the University's *Excerpta e Statutis*, reproduced at the end of this chapter in Appendix 14A.

Having been delighted to find how much physics was involved in radio, I had intended to opt for advanced electromagnetism but was diverted from this course by Lindemann, whom I had somewhat accidentally impressed by answers to questions that he himself had set in the informal papers 'Collection' that all physics students had to sit at the end of each Michaelmas (autumn) term and Hilary (spring) term, irrespective of whether they had been reading physics for one, two, or three years. Lindemann's questions were of a different type from those set by the lecturers and demonstrators, and I was fascinated by the challenge that they presented. It turned out that he was looking for what the classicists called *spes* (hope) rather than *res* (things) in us and his questions were designed to provoke us into thought so that he might detect any flashes of physical insight and assess our approach to physical situations that we were unlikely to have previously encountered, and from which he might be able to spot any potential talent we might have as research students. I can hardly remember any of his questions precisely enough to reproduce it here, but they had such an effect on me that I followed his practice when I went to Aberdeen, where I found that they provided a truer criterion of a student's potential for research than even a first-class performance in the papers set on conventional lines. A few examples of such questions, to show their types, can be found in Appendix 14B.

As a result of my attempts at his questions, Lindemann evidently decided that I might have prospects as a research student. He even spoke of something then beyond my dreams—a Fellowship. There were only about six Fellowships in physics in the entire University, and one would only become vacant every five or so years. When he asked me what advanced subject I proposed to offer in Honours, I told him that I hoped to do electromagnetism because of my interest in electronics. 'Oh', he said, 'you don't want to do that—it's just the same old differential equation over and over again.' Duly impressed, because his experience was far above mine, I decided that I must therefore choose one of the other two specialities. In retrospect, and having regard to the fact that subsequent developments in electronics showed my judgement to be at least as good as his, I think that what he was really saying was that if I took electromagnetism I would be lost to him because I would become Townsend's research student in the Electrical Laboratory† rather than his in the Clarendon; but my die was now cast.

When I considered the choice between the other two subjects, I noted that nearly all candidates opted for atomic physics. I thought that the unpopularity of statistical physics might be due to its intrinsic difficulty, and so I responded to the challenge. The immediate problem that I encountered was that my tutor, who was primarily a specialist in practical work, knew little of statistical physics and so I had in the main to teach myself, mainly from the few available textbooks, such as those of Brillouin and Tolman, backed up by some of Lindemann's own lectures. At the time he was enthusiastic about the Uncertainty Principle which Heisenberg had formulated only three or four years before, and he was applying it with great ingenuity, and indeed elegance, to a variety of physical phenomena. We also met Einstein–Bose and Fermi–Dirac statistics, which had only been formulated as recently as 1924 and 1926, and, surprisingly perhaps, I had already learnt of G P Thomson's demonstration of the wave nature of the electron in 1928 while I was still at school, and his experiment had only been published in 1927. We were, of course, expected to know the classical statistics of Maxwell and Boltzmann, and to be able to show the relation between probability and entropy.

A further difficulty to be faced was the fact that none of the three members of the examining board when I took finals was versed in statistical physics, and I had noted a trend for the special papers in that subject to include a rising proportion of questions that had primarily been set for the other two subjects. This meant that one's choice of questions truly inside the statistical syllabus was not from nine but, to judge by the 1931 or 1930 papers, merely from four or five. In 1932,

† Although the Electrical Laboratory was less lively than the Clarendon, its practical courses introduced us to some interesting experiments, especially on electricity in gases, radioactivity and microwaves. One of the demonstrators was E W B Gill, who had been a signals officer in World War I and who, with another demonstrator, had discovered Gill–Morrell oscillations (also known as Barkhausen–Kurz) on about 60 centimetres, which we used in the microwave experiments.

when I sat finals, there were in fact only two in the first statistical paper and, I think, four in the second. In the first paper there was even a question on atomic physics that was not in either of the atomic physics papers, so cavalier had the examiners become. There was a protest which resulted in the papers in the subsequent years being much more conscientiously set; and there was also another protest, incidentally, because the papers included a question on the neutron which had been discovered only a few months before.

While the examiners had obviously been perfunctory in their attitude towards the papers, we candidates knew that our answers would determine our future careers, especially since in 1932 we were at the height of the great depression that had started in 1929 and competition for postgraduate studentships and for outside employment was severe. Of the twenty or so of my contemporaries who sat the examination, I reckoned that ten would have good chances of reaching a first-class standard if the questions fell their way, but that on the records of previous years no more than four, or at the outside five, Firsts would be awarded. So most of us worked desperately; and the strain told. One who might well have got a First had a complete breakdown in the papers and was unable to write a word, and another collapsed to a Third Class. The most tragic case was someone who had obtained a First in mathematical moderations, but who now collapsed to a Fourth in physics and was committed to an asylum with a deranged mind. Some months afterwards the contemporary, who had been his partner in practical work and who was now a research student, received a card from him, written in the asylum, which enigmatically ran: 'Dear Douglas, This is a marvellous place, where I am king by day and queen by night!' I kept memories of such misfortunes in mind when it became my own turn to set examination papers.

In the event, five of us were awarded First Class Honours, and three, together with one who had a Second but who was well regarded by Lindemann, stayed on for research. Again, as in the setting of finals papers, 1932 was a watershed, for we were the last group to be set on to problems in nearly random directions rarely connected with one another in any form of concerted programme. The random nature of our problems largely reflected the diversity of Lindemann's interests in physics, which was also reflected in his own contributions. For one, there was the Lindemann melting-point formula for crystals: for another, there was the Nernst–Lindemann theory of specific heats, backed up by their measurements at low temperature: with his father and brother he had made a Lindemann glass for transmitting x-rays, and with Aston in 1919 he had devised methods of separating isotopes: he also had a theory of electrical conduction based on the concept of a lattice of electrons moving through a lattice of metallic ions. After he came to Oxford he had designed with his father and T C Keeley the Lindemann electrometer, which came into worldwide use, and with G M B Dobson he had recognised (on the basis of observation of the propagation of sound waves to great distances from explosions in World War I) that there must be a high-temperature layer in the upper atmosphere.

He had, however, few staff to support him, and he obviously set successive years of research students off as prospectors in various fields of physics, while—except for Indeterminacy—he himself did increasingly little. We had no postgraduate training—we were just 'chucked in at the deep end' and we either sank or swam. One *pons asinorum* that most of us were expected to cross was the construction of a vacuum system where we had to blow all the necessary components including water-pumps (rotary pumps were too expensive) and liquid-air traps, but excluding mercury vapour pumps and stop-cocks. There was a story in my time of a research student in an earlier year who had built his vacuum system competently enough but who was troubled by the explosive boiling of the mercury which made the pump 'bump' and the whole system vibrate. When Lindemann asked him about his progress, he mentioned his difficulty. 'Ah' said Lindemann 'I've always wondered what makes pumps bump—you ought to investigate it!' The student went back to his room and worked away for months until he thought he had found the reason, having in the meantime been careful to keep out of the Professor's way for fear of being castigated for lack of progress. He then emerged to greet the Professor with 'I now have the answer to why pumps bump' only to be withered by Lindemann's 'Why ever have you been spending your time on a trivial problem like that?'

Lindemann's approach had its successes. E Bolton King and T C Keeley produced the best photocells in the world. R d'E Atkinson paralleled Bethe and von Weizsäcker in formulating the hydrogen-helium cycle for thermonuclear energy. A H Holbourn determined the angular momentum of a photon and J H E Griffiths measured the lifetimes of helium atoms in excited states. Griffiths was one of the best experimenters ever to be produced in the Clarendon and, incidentally, held it as his greatest triumph as an examiner to insist on Martin Ryle being awarded a First solely on the strength of his performance in the practical examination. Atkinson was lost to Oxford despite his brilliance because—so Lindemann told me as a warning—his argumentative forthrightness was hardly acceptable in an Oxford SCR atmosphere. Such a propensity, however, did not prevent Lindemann inviting to Oxford D A Jackson, a Cambridge graduate who, against Rutherford's wishes, wanted to work in spectroscopy. DA's identical twin, CV, by contrast had graduated at Oxford but went off to work, also in spectroscopy, with Arthur Fowler at Imperial College.

Both the Jacksons were true physicists. They had no need to work, since their wealth included a substantial share in the interests of *The News of the World*. I once asked Derek why he took up spectroscopy and met with the reply 'Why, man, you must have something to do in the summer, when you can't hunt!': and his riding was as impressive as his spectroscopy, for he both rode in the Grand National and became a Fellow of the Royal Society. In fact, several of us had dual interests: two Canadian Rhodes Scholars, Gratias and Babbitt, achieved Doctorates as well as 'blues' for ice hockey; J H E Griffiths was an oarsman of Leander quality; A H S Holbourn was in the Merton first eight; R A Hull was an outstanding mountaineer who was later killed by a rock-fall on Mont Blanc; T Bourdillon very nearly reached the top of Everest in the 1953 expedition; and Lindemann himself had won numerous tennis tournaments on the continent, including a championship in Sweden. Yet all these outside distinctions were achieved by a research staff which numbered less than twenty.

As a whole, though, in 1932 the Clarendon was still searching for a theme on which to concentrate. It made one or two attempts to rival the Cavendish, and until recently I had tended to blame Lindemann for the rivalry, for it would have seemed better for the two laboratories to specialise in different branches, especially so that with our relatively few physicists we should not have all our national eggs in one basket; and since Rutherford was so outstanding in nuclear physics that field should be left entirely to him. I have recently found that Lindemann had had a similar idea, and had actually written to Rutherford in 1919 shortly after each had been elected to their respective Chairs in Oxford and Cambridge: 'I am most anxious to work in the closest cooperation with Cambridge and the other schools of physics, both to prevent overlapping and because I believe there is no stimulus to new ideas like personal intercourse with other workers in allied branches.' Nothing came of this approach, and rivalry tended to develop.

Following the discovery of heavy water in 1933, there were frenzied efforts in the Clarendon to find new ways of separating it—Lindemann thought that the Dead Sea might be a promising source because heavy water would evaporate slightly less easily than light, while his senior demonstrator, knowing that the heavy hydrogen isotope could be concentrated by electrolysis, achieved a dramatic if futile result by connecting the AC mains across an electrolytic cell. It was fair enough for Lindemann to 'stake a claim' in isotope separation because of his work with Aston on possible methods in 1919, when few others had even conceived the possibility. Similarly, his earlier work on low-temperature measurements justified his taking up low temperatures again in 1933; he invited K A G Mendelssohn over from Germany to put into operation a helium liquefier that had been purchased from Mendelssohn's professor, F E Simon. From what Lindemann said to me at the time, I am sure that at least part of his motive was to 'wipe the eye' of the Cavendish because he was upset by the large grant made to Cambridge to enable Kapitza to develop the Mond Laboratory. As a sign of its success, at its inauguration the Mond was expected to liquefy helium 'for the first time in Britain' but by the time it opened in February 1933 the Mond had been anticipated by several weeks.

The liquefaction of helium signalled a change in the fortunes of the Clarendon; by itself it might have been of little effect, but within a few months there was a great exodus of the Jewish scientists from Germany, driven by well-founded fears of what their fate might be if they stayed in Nazi Germany. Lindemann, who closely followed the development of events there, promptly offered the hospitality of the Clarendon to as many as, and indeed more than, it could accommodate. In particular he invited F E Simon and his low-temperature team including Mendelssohn and N Kurti, and the two London Brothers, Fritz and Heinz. E Schrödinger also came, as did L Szilard and H Kuhn. Of these, Simon, Kurti, Mendelssohn and Kuhn became permanent members of the Clarendon staff and made many contributions, of which the first was the Rollin–Simon film that pointed to the existence of superfluid helium II. B V Rollin, who had come up as an undergraduate to Wadham a year after me, started as a research student in 1933 and was the first of our native graduates to work with Simon: he proved to be a remarkably able experimenter.

We still had no formal postgraduate lectures. The main effect of the influx from Germany was not in that direction, but more towards the 'master–apprentice' relation between an acknowledged leader and his research students, instead of the 'chucking in at the deep end' which had been the experience of all previous research students up to my own year. We had had, of course, some lectures and seminars that were primarily directed towards postgraduates: for example, E A Milne, the Professor of Applied Mathematics, ran a weekly evening colloquium in his rooms in Wadham which as many as twenty of us might attend, along with any eminent visitor whom he could attract. I remember one occasion, for example, where Einstein spoke, and the astronomer H N Russell was also present; and there was another when Milne himself announced for the first time his formulation of kinematic relativity, where he conceived an expanding universe which, because of the relationships of special relativity, would look the same to observers wherever they were in it—so that each might conclude that he was at the centre.

Milne's ideas had been stimulated by Hubble's recent discovery of the apparent recession of the galaxies—and Hubble was yet another of those who lectured to us, as was Bohr. In fact we were remarkably fortunate in the cavalcade of world figures who for one reason or another passed through Oxford, usually invited by Lindemann or Milne, and whom we—even as undergraduates—were able to question. I recall asking Einstein in 1931 whether he thought that the galaxies were really receding or whether the red-shift was somehow an effect of distance. Einstein replied that he could not be sure, but, if I understood him aright, he liked to think of the photons becoming tired as they were buffeted in their journey through space.

Rutherford came across occasionally from Cambridge, and his lectures were always memorable. In the question session after one of them E A Milne asked for his views on what was known as the Tutin atom. This concept had been started by a Dr Tutin, who argued that the Rutherford model of the atom was all wrong, for everyone knew that if you spin a mixture of light and heavy particles, the heavy ones fly to the outside while the light ones stay close to the centre. So in an atom the electrons should be in the middle with the protons orbiting outside. The theory had achieved notoriety because F W Soddy, the Professor of Inorganic Chemistry, who had given isotopes their name, had communicated Tutin's paper to the Chemical Society, which had refused to publish the paper in its Journal, whereupon Soddy had resigned from the Society and had promptly advertised the sale of all his volumes of *Journal of the Chemical Society* in *Nature*. Milne asked Rutherford how he could be sure that Tutin was wrong and he was right. I can still see Rutherford, who was a big man, bending over towards Milne, who was a small one, and booming 'When you've got an elephant and a flea, you assume it's the flea that jumps.'

The nearest to a formal course of postgraduate lectures that occurred in my time was when Schrödinger gave a series on wave mechanics. This was a marvellous opportunity, but few of us had the mathematical equipment to appreciate it. Schrödinger and F London left after two or three years, dissatisfied—so I was told—by the financial support available to them. As for our own financial support, the London County Council made up my undergraduate grant to £240 per annum, equivalent to about £4800 today, which was just enough to pay my way for the three eight-week terms at Oxford, with nothing left to cover vacations, and in the Depression there was little possibility of vacation employment. As research students, our annual grants were £250, or £5000 in present-day terms; since graduation we were permitted to live in unlicensed lodgings, which were generally cheaper, we could then afford to stay in Oxford for 48 or more weeks in the year. Grants were in general available only for the shortest possible period in which it was possible to qualify for the appropriate degree—two years in the case of a Doctorate in philosophy. While this was an impressive stimulus to hard work (some of us might be found in the laboratory at 3 o'clock in the morning, or even working all night—although since Lindemann himself never appeared before 11.00 AM, few of us would anticipate

him by more than half an hour) it also had the drawback of forcing us
to work on short-term problems when it would in some instances have
been advantageous to go for problems which might require a year or
more spent in acquiring the theoretical equipment with which to tackle
them. Driven by financial necessity I myself, for example, qualified for
a Doctorate well before my twenty-third birthday: it was exhilarating
though, especially since I could then take myself and my friends (who
still being *in statu pupillari* were now nominally in my care as a 'learned
master' of the university) into a public house, which was forbidden even
to those of whatever age with only bachelors' degrees. But in retrospect
I wish that I could have spent more time taking a Doctorate and in attaining a much better command of theoretical physics in the process.

All in all, though, it was a fascinating time to come into physics, on
the coat-tails of relativity and the even more recent quantum mechanics,
with the discoveries of the neutron and the positive electron and
artificial radioactivity, and the Cockcroft–Walton experiment, and—
although hardly anyone noticed it at the time—Jansky's discovery of
cosmic radio noise. In applied physics, television was coming healthily
along, and—for those of us involved—radar and nuclear fission.
Moreover, even the most junior of us would have had the opportunity
of seeing, and listening to, many of the principal figures in physics.
While working hard and being far from care-free, we enjoyed ourselves
to the full, and the laboratory was a lively place where humour bubbled
over. But as we watched the rise of Nazi Germany some of us foresaw
that our physics would be needed for grimmer days.

When war came Derek Jackson took his skill in observation and in the
hunt into nightfighters, becoming Chief Airborne Radar Officer at
Fighter Command. Gerald Touch had left as early as 1936 to join
Watson-Watt's radar team at Bawdsey, where he developed airborne
radar for maritime use. In 1942 James Griffiths, after working in the
laboratory on radar problems, went to the Admiralty as Secretary of the
Committee on Valve Development. C G Wynne, who had gone into the
optical industry, designed lenses for high-performance cameras for the
RAF's photographic reconnaissance aircraft. B V Rollin stayed in the
Clarendon to develop the reflex klystron and A H Cooke and others
worked there on microwaves, while Martin Ryle went to Malvern where
he joined the group in electronic warfare. F E Simon, N Kurti and H
S Arms (an American) also stayed in the Clarendon, working on isotope
separation for the nuclear energy project, developing in particular
porous metallic membranes for the thermal diffusion method.
Lindemann himself, of course, went to Whitehall as Churchill's scientific adviser, taking with him J L Tuck who, finding a desk existence too
dull, escaped in 1941 to work in 'Winston Churchill's Toyshop'—the
establishment known as MD 1 where unconventional weapons were

developed and where his speciality was the 'hollow charge'. From there he went to Los Alamos in 1943, where his experiences with focused shock-waves enabled plutonium to be successfully imploded. In fact, Bruno Rossi told me that it is doubtful whether the plutonium bomb could have been detonated in 1945 without Tuck's contribution.

If the main object of a university education is to equip those who graduate from it so that they are able to deal with situations for which there are no direct precedents, then the diverse contributions of Oxford physicists in the war showed that their education, while far from perfect, at least measured up to this important test. Obviously the system had to change, for physics had already expanded far beyond the range of any one tutor, and it had advanced so far that some degree of postgraduate instruction was needed before the budding physicist had enough theoretical equipment to make an original contribution. But there will always have to be a compromise between a zeal for formal instruction and the need to get a physicist into a research atmosphere where his mental alertness in the front-line will not have been dulled by too long a route-march through territory already won.

Appendix 14A: An outline of the syllabus of specialised subjects for Honours candidates (*Excerpta e Statutis*)

Advanced Electromagnetism
Electrical oscillations; Maxwell's theory; Propagation, reflection, refraction, dispersion, polarization of electromagnetic waves including light; Oscillatory circuits; Valves and valve circuits; Radiating and receiving circuits; Damped and continuous waves; Methods of measuring wavelength, refraction, dispersion and polarization; Relativity.

Statistical Physics
Entropy and probability; Kinetic theory; Electrolysis; Metallic conduction; Heats of reaction—Thermodynamics; Chemical constants.

Atomic Physics
Properties of electrons and positive ions; Ionization and conduction of electricity in gases; Periodic table; Radio-activity; Atomic structure; Spectral series; Fine structure, Zeeman and Stark effects, and interferometer methods of measuring them; X-rays; Photo-electricity.

Appendix 14B: Examples of questions similar to those set to find an undergraduate's potential as a research student

(1) It is an accepted fact that a long chimney creates a stronger draught

than a short one. Assuming that this is so, advance a possible explanation.

(2) 'There are three things which are too wonderful for me, yea, four which I know not:

The way of an eagle in the air; the way of a serpent upon a rock; the way of a ship in the midst of the sea; and the way of a man with a maid.' (Proverbs 30: 18–19)

What explanation would you give to Solomon for any three of the foregoing?

(3) A standard test to find whether a long focus lens is positive or negative is to view a distant object through it, when it is held near the eye, and to move the lens transversely to the direction of the object. If the object, as viewed through the lens, moves in the same direction as the lens, the lens is negative: if the motion is in the opposite direction the lens is positive. Why is this?

(4) When a toy gyroscope is spinning with its axis inclined to the vertical, and is supported on a single pivot at the lower end of the axis, so that it precesses under gravity, would you expect there to be a horizontal reaction on the pivot or not, and why?

If your conclusion disagrees with that of a Professor of Electrical Engineering who contends that there is no horizontal reaction, how would you attempt to convince him by a practical demonstration? (He has already tried the experiment with the pivot and its base resting on a horizontal surface of ice, and thinks that he has found that there is no tendency for the base to slip sideways as the gyroscope precesses).

(5) Is it possible, by repeated use of a ruler divided into millimetres, and reading the positions of the scale divisions nearest to the ends on a linear object, to deduce from these readings the length of the object to a precision of, say, one tenth or one hundredth of a millimetre?

Mark two dots a convenient distance apart on your examination script. Using the centimetre divisions only on your ruler, apply your method to measure the distance between the dots with a precision of two millimetres.

CHAPTER FIFTEEN

STUDENT DAYS AND APPRENTICESHIP WITH CTR

J G Wilson

I went up to Cambridge in October 1929, but after taking Part I in 1931 my progress was interrupted by a prolonged spell of illness, and I did not do Part II (physics) until 1933. Then I became a research student under C T R Wilson (no relation) until 1936 when I left Cambridge to work with Patrick Blackett in London. My Part I was in mathematics, physics and chemistry, a combination in which the basic timetable occupied six mornings a week, from 9 AM to 1 PM. People of real ability in mathematics normally read for the Mathematical Tripos. My mathematical attainment when I went up could at best be described as 'fairly sound', and this went also for most of my friends, so experimental physics and theoretical physics were at that time tending to recruit, and so to develop, along separate ways. The chemistry Part I lecture class was a large one, for there was a considerable chemistry–biological stream, and the atmosphere tended to be pretty relaxed, high spirits peaking on such days as 5 November. The selective element was provided by admission to the 'Scholars' Laboratory' for practical work, in which the level of staffing was generous, where one had the exclusive use of a bench and where one carried out organic preparations in sufficient quantity to be able to do something with the product. The price for this privilege was an increased bill for materials and the extension of laboratory time into several afternoons a week. Although I never had any intention of becoming a chemist, I am glad that I did this.

The basic Part I lectures in physics and mathematics were directed very much towards areas which many of us imagined we had fully mastered at school. I cannot recall any, given the level of understanding towards which they were aimed, which were not good, but the only lecturer from that time (apart from those who come into my recollection in other contexts) who did unquestionably sparkle (and so on occasion could bring the house down) was Alex Wood of Emmanuel. But during this time my real initiation into physics came from college supervision, with weekly tutorials from Jack Ratcliffe in physics and Gordon Welchman in mathematics. Welchman was the first real mathematician I had ever met, and it was my good fortune that his brilliance did not dim his understanding of the needs of people like me. What he gave me was a sort of 'users' guide' to mathematics, the most effective formulation of mathematical problems and the sort of solutions that could come from them. Mathematical elegance emerged as something where appropriateness was the key.

I did not know, of course, that my contacts with Jack Ratcliffe were to extend for upwards of half a century, during which almost all our thoughts about physics have changed. In college supervisions he focused one's mind on what was becoming important in the development of physics: he would argue at length about topics which were really puzzling everybody; the relation of magnetic force and induction, the dimensions of electrons in nuclei (later in this article I mention Gamow's book; he also found this feature challenging), the wave–particle duality as it applies in simple diffraction phenomena and the relation of Dirac's theory of electrons with physical reality. We talked about the development of the wave-mechanical description from the Bohr model of the hydrogen atom, and I think it was here that I began to understand the satisfaction stemming from the elimination of *ad hoc* elements from a mainly effective model. He was often full of recent data and thoughts about the transmission of radio waves in the ionosphere (his speciality) and finally he persuaded me (against my initial inclination) to go to J J Thomson's lecture course, perhaps a very early induction into the modern cult of personal recollections!

Since the few lecture notes which I have kept neglect to state the year, even when otherwise dated, I cannot confirm my recollections of lecture courses as either in the Part II year or in my following graduate time. However those of Rutherford himself and of John Cockcroft were certainly Part II lectures, and brilliant in their contrasting styles. The natural warmth of Rutherford's lecturing seemed even enhanced when he was lecturing to his own undergraduates, and on themes which had been his own from their very inception. Cockcroft was much more restrained. He lectured on electromagnetic theory, and in vector notation: I am not sure whether he realised that for many of us this was here being seriously used for the first time, but as he set out the basic equations, and their relationships, the whole which emerged was elegantly convincing. A little later Max Born spent some time in Cambridge when first he was driven out of Germany. He lectured out of a little black notebook on electromagnetic theory using cartesian notation, and I have to admit that I found this alternative presentation helpful.

A lecture course certainly given before I took Part II was A H Wilson's in Emmanuel, listed in the *Reporter* as on the 'Theory of Metals': in fact it developed the theory of semiconductors, and to a level which was quite new to me. Among other courses which I must have attended before I graduated was C T R Wilson's on 'Condensation on Nuclei'. His greatest admirers dare not describe his conventional lecturing manner as anything but quite dreadful: his quiet voice was directed to the blackboard, he wrote very faintly and moved in front of what he had written as he went on. In his left hand was a duster, and when his writing did emerge from behind him it was instantly rubbed out. But the matter was priceless, and very much more distinguished people than I, for example Patrick Blackett and Cecil Powell, would recall these lectures with enthusiasm. What was certainly a graduate course for me, although it may well have been primarily for a special subject in Part II of the Mathematical Tripos, was R H Fowler's 'Statistical Mechanics'. His mastery of the material and the vigour and enthusiasm of his presentation were recipes for understanding: I still have my lecture notes from the course and these retain a great deal of the virtue of the original.

The books we used were a very mixed bag and reflected the rapid advance, then in full flood, in atomic physics and the relative but certainly not absolute stagnation in other areas of the subject. Among books in this second category the *Physical Optics* of R W Wood, who held the Chair of Experimental Physics at Johns Hopkins, fascinated me; he was much more thoroughly familiar with the work of the French workers than other writers of his time, but above all he had the unmistakable approach of a natural experimentalist. Textbooks in atomic physics, attempting a balanced understanding over the whole field as opposed to monographs on limited topics, were only beginning to become important in my time and for these the quality of the work was at least as important as the breadth of cover. Mott's *Outline of Wave Mechanics* (1930) could hardly have appeared earlier, while Rutherford, Chadwick and Ellis's major work, *Radioactive Substances and their Radiations*, also of that year, had developed almost out of recognition from Rutherford's 1913 book, which had much of the quality of a monograph. But some works which were quite masterly in their presentation were fated to be unfortunate. Gamow's *Atomic Nuclei and Radioactivity* came out in 1931, and covered exhaustive references to experimental material right up to that year. Alas! Within a very short time the discovery of the neutron undermined the whole forward-looking approach so carefully developed. This notable work illustrates the very shaky ground on which authors at the time stood. While today one can appreciate the quality which went into shaping the argument, and understand the problems which were facing people at the time, my recollections are that this is not how young people treated it: it was easy to dismiss it as outdated—outdated in six months! (Almost unbelievably, the almost entirely rewritten second edition suffered a rather similar fate.) It is not possible to dip into these books and others like them without wondering whether students of today are as well served as they might be. Many factors are working against that possibility. Now readers come up to the level of a broad and authoritative textbook with a far more varied range of preparation, and face an explosively developing range of material, while the required levels of mathematical argument seem to be changing almost as quickly. Serious problems unknown, or nearly so, fifty years ago were first the problem of continuity (for atomic physics from the 'classical' era of the 1890s) and secondly the maintenance of a writing style, faltering under the load of reference material which some people now regard as obligatory. But these are matters which cannot be followed here.

The three practical classes covered by Part I and then Part II were all very different, but came to one in essentially the correct order. Almost the whole of G F C Searle's class would have been appropriate in 1890, and concentrated on accuracy of individual measurements following an explicitly laid-down procedure. This was the only class which had what appeared to be purpose-built equipment, particularly a standard form of optical bench and geometrically designed slides for use with them. There was also a very ingenious arrangement of brass tubes, coaxial and about 2 cm in diameter, between which soap films could be blown and for which conditions of instability established.

The second year laboratory, under C D Ellis, was very different: you were set an objective but given little or no guidance as to how to get there. When you were stuck (and you quite often were) Ellis would ruffle through a set of much-used single sheets in his desk: 'I think you may find this will help.' And it did, up to a point! While further doles of help were available, you soon grasped the message. I do not think there was anything purpose-built here, but most laboratories at the time must have accumulated a collection of standard, if dated, electrical components, and the range of experiments was devised to use what was to hand. Again in this laboratory I cannot recall anything which had much to do with 'modern physics' as it was (in all seriousness) described.

It was in the Part II practical class that one was brought to the threshold of modern times, and all the best items from the past which remained serviceable seemed to have gravitated there. Surveying what was in use there at the time, I have been intrigued to find that the experiment on the dispersion of cyanin (see below) brought together two spectrometers each of which was a much finer instrument than any existing in the whole department at Leeds at any time in the last thirty years! When and why these had ever been obtained I do not know. There was one instance in which equipment was plainly purpose-built, and for obvious reasons. This consisted of a number of light-metal cast box frames with windows through which reading microscopes could be used. When one of these was furnished with a pair of 'gold leaves', which were in fact Dutch metal, and a large Dutch metal sheet window in the base, it formed an electroscope which was standard for a variety of experiments on ionisation. The store of available equipment was surely the legacy of the succession of Directors who had run the class over the years. Naturally, the most recent times were most heavily represented, and here I was fortunate, for the range of experiments in physical optics, which I think owed a lot to Patrick Blackett, had a special attraction for me. These covered most of the important interferometers and their application to measures of resolving power, and fine structure; also, measurements of polarisation at scattering in a suspension of colloidal silver, and in a more complex way, the measurement of changes of polarisation of light reflected at polished metal surfaces. A high point of this excursion into physical optics came by carrying out R W Wood's experiment on the anomalous dispersion of fused cyanin in a developed and quantitative way.

At that time it was not yet possible to prepare artificial radioactive materials and so the choice of suitable sources for laboratory experiments was pretty limited. The variation of ionisation along the last two centimetres or so of the range of polonium alpha-particles could be followed in a very thin ion chamber, and this observation provided an opportunity to use a quadrant electrometer (I think an antique even then); an obvious extension led to measurements of the stopping power of metal foils. The short-term activity of a source involving successive active elements was followed using the standard form of gold-leaf electroscope and as sources preparations of actinium active deposit (effectively AcB and AcC) providing both short—and relatively long—activities.

The few weeks of the summer term before the Tripos were kept free of lectures but not of conflicting advice about revision. Probably the wisest stressed quality against quantity: 'two hours a day, but let it be intense!' I am not sure that my recollections about the Tripos are accurate, but they are probably broadly correct. There were six written papers, taken morning and afternoon on three successive days; I do not think that the scope of individual papers was indicated, so there was little temptation to cram in any revision day by day. At the end one felt completely washed out, and all the plans made to celebrate went for nothing. The Class lists for the Tripos were published fairly quickly, and providing you got a First your research studentship was pretty well assured. Plans with your prospective supervisor and your plan of work could not be settled (at any rate formally) until October, so fresh research students who had grown up in the Cavendish spent the long-vacation term that year in what was known as the 'Nursery'. This was a large attic room in the older part of the laboratory and it was unbearably hot in summer. Here you got to know your immediate contemporaries, whom you could hardly have met easily in the large Part II class, undertook some minor problem and talked a great deal. Chadwick was Director of Research, and as a duty visited the Nursery most days. But he seemed to dislike the heat as much as we did so his visits were not often prolonged. My own objective was to measure the radioactivity of rainwater, on which the literature was very thin, and this promised to be really interesting. However, it did not rain at all the whole time!

It never occurred to me to be curious about the way in which other people found their way into their particular line of work, but I have no doubt that my own course was mapped out in College: Jack Ratcliffe persuaded 'CTR' that I would suit him and that I was keen to come—an understatement if ever there was one! (I ought to explain that all three of us were members of the same College.) I suppose that this arrangement must have been endorsed somewhere.

During one's career as a research student one's own experiences were so vivid, and your knowledge of what other people were doing so fragmentary, that what it is possible to write about now, fifty years later, is firstly the general conditions in which one lived and worked in those days, at any rate in Cambridge, and secondly the impressions which remain clear about what one did oneself. A single exception to this separation, interesting because it dates us, concerns an exact contemporary of mine, whose plan was to start his work by making some Geiger (tube) counters, following a brief reference to these which made the construction sound easy. Plainly the account did not bring out the difficulties; the victim was inclined to attribute to cunning secrecy what I think, with hindsight, was only ignorance.

In the mid-1930s early marriage was discouraged, and indeed there were many professions—the Civil Service, teaching and in universities where women were able to take up regular lecturing posts—from which women were required to resign on marriage. In Cambridge women students were segregated in their own Colleges and in any case did not show any enthusiasm for physical science. It is not surprising, therefore, that research students at the Cavendish were almost without exception single men with College-centred interests. At levels of seniority where people were coming in from elsewhere some were married and I think there were one or two women researchers, but these were not numerous enough nor quite in the right place to affect the general picture. This said, I am inclined to think that these factors, whatever might be thought of them fifty years later, yielded a climate very favourable to the professional development of those caught up in the system. Particularly in a college of modest size there tended to grow up a clique of science research students, often describing themselves as a club, which would gather when they were not actually working and whose exchanges provided a valuable measure of cross-fertilisation; these were people too who readily understood when one shut oneself off to work.

In the laboratory, where there were so many internationally known people working, and when the time-scale of significant work was so short (perhaps of the order of a single year or less), extended projects, maintained over a term of years by successive entries of students, were hardly thought of: the norm was a much simpler relation between student and what he was trying to do. While our materials were no longer string and sealing-wax, they could none the less be abnormal and outside common workshop practice. However, each Monday morning in our first research term we were gathered together to gain experience in simple workshop operations: shaping, soldering and brazing pieces of brass (from the scrap box) cutting screws on rods and tapping holes in plates. We bought our hand-tools in the town, and most of us went for the cheapest we could find. The high point of this experience came when we made our own hand-tools for metal-turning; grinding, tempering and sharpening them.

There must have been far less necessary reading then than there is today, but I think that in proportion to what was desirable, people bought more books. The circulation of preprints was virtually unknown, so for keeping up to date one was very dependent on the principal journals as they reached the laboratory. But even then the dominance of much American work was beginning to be apparent, and many of us became members of the American Physical Society, for this ensured that our own copy of the *Physical Review* (in those days undivided) arrived regularly: you were spared the irritation of chasing library copies, and you could read and re-read important material at your convenience. While there were limited opportunities of getting to meetings in this country, made easier if you were reasonably near to London, international conferences were right outside the experience of practically all junior researchers. Altogether, there were, of course, very few of these.

I was introduced to a problem which was to spill over in a different guise after I had left Cambridge to work in London. The photographed tracks of single cosmic ray particles in a steady magnetic field, achieved by Blackett and Occhialini, allowed the momentum of particles detected in this way to be determined. But the curvatures measured tended to be very small, and anything that could be done to increase them needed to be explored. An obvious step was to minimise the volume of the air gap in the magnetic circuit and my objective was to devise a thin cloud chamber which would fit into the smallest possible air gap, and which after discharge could be withdrawn from the magnet for the tracks to be photographed. So far, this was a plan to increase the magnetic field, causing greater curvature of tracks, but at the same time it was necessary to minimise track distortions due to gas motions in the chamber. One of the first of these which came to mind was the convection set up by the temperature difference between the gas, cooled by sudden expansion, and the uncooled solid walls of the cloud chamber. For the suppression of this particular gas motion only (ignoring others) it was sufficient to withdraw the chamber by allowing it to fall freely!

Attempting to achieve this led to an experimental system rather than a prototype: the back and front walls of the chamber were glass, and photographs were taken with light passing right through the chamber, with small-angle forward scattering from the track droplets; expansion was radial, through a cylindrical porous wall. The rest of the apparatus was peculiar-looking but it operated successfully both at rest and in free fall; not only was the intended suppression of gross convection achieved but also, and I think for the first time, the whole volume of gas remaining in the chamber after expansion, and its motions, could be studied. A reliable mode of bringing the falling chamber to rest gave no trouble whatever, but possible failure provided some of my friends with material for rather tedious jokes. The limited objective had been achieved, but in the longer term attention directed to other modes of gas motion proved more important, and was of continued value for my work in London.

Two characteristics which remain in my mind from supervision by 'CTR' are on the one hand the fertility with which he came up with logical, but at first sight quite impractical, suggestions about work in progress and on the other, quite separately, times when he would speculate on all manner of aspects of cloud formation and of optical phenomena associated with cloud droplets. I remember particularly talks we had at those times about nucleation for drop formation in dust-free (and ion-free) gas.

The use of a pile of slate annuli separated by mica spacers as a cylindrical porous wall was entirely successful, for the spacers could be adjusted to give the required gas flow characteristics. But I do not think that 'CTR' had ever turned annuli from thin slates. It was I who had to meet the continued disapproval of the Head of the Workshop, who did not like people who spread slate dust over his better lathes. Another at first sight daunting operation relating to a different radial-expansion chamber was to examine the gas motion at expansion by photography through a narrow slit onto a rotating drum. (We did not have such a camera, so as a preliminary I had to make one.) What was photographed was the thinnest possible sliver of mica that I could separate, suspended by spider threads! Providing one kept calm, this turned out to be less difficult than I had expected, but a lot depended on the frame of mind of your spiders.

These examples stay in mind because they are a little exotic, but they illustrate a general feature of the work of young research students at the time: while such things as stop-clocks and reading microscopes were available from the laboratory stock, one approached one's early investigations expecting to have to make what was special to the job. I think that this was good for one, but it is as memorable for illustrating the atmosphere of economy which was sustained.

CHAPTER SIXTEEN

THE SCOTTISH SCENE IN THE INTER-WAR YEARS

Sir Samuel Curran

Introductory Remarks

My personal memories of school are very clear from the age of four, which means that so far as education is concerned I recall personally features of Scottish education back to 1916. Naturally the educational pattern did not affect me critically till somewhat later but a few words about Scottish schools are important when we come to consider the influence of physics in the inter-war years. I will try to say briefly what I believe is important about the similarities and differences between the Scottish and English school patterns.

In the inter-war years much of the preparation of scholars who would pursue science in the universities was done in 'public schools' in England, but in Scotland the vast majority of such students were taught in State schools. Due to the difficult economic climate the teachers in the High Schools or Secondary Schools were very well qualified. There was no over-supply in the 'difficult' subjects, namely mathematics and physics, but there was just an adequate provision of teachers with Honours degree qualifications for the principal Secondary Schools. The supply of graduates with Honours in chemistry was more abundant and many of the Honours chemistry graduates were in charge of the 'science' instruction in the schools. This was possibly a weakness in the teaching of science because even as a young student I realised that the teachers were not as thoroughly equipped to teach physics as they might have been.

A few words of explanation are needed here because another matter of importance in schools was due to the tendency in Scottish universities to provide combined Honours degrees. The combination of mathematics and physics was a well accepted one and indeed in Glasgow University single Honours in mathematics was not offered. The Master of Arts with Honours was given in those days in mathematics and natural philosophy and usually three of the five papers in the Finals of natural philosophy were taken in the MA examination. The pattern has changed in more recent times but we should note here that there were features giving both strength and weakness in schools and universities of the inter-war period. In the schools, as I have said, one of the principal subjects of instruction was labelled 'science' and usually it consisted of equal parts of physics and chemistry but all of it was normally taught by men with an Honours qualification in chemistry and at most one or two years of university study of physics, the physics being the subsidiary subject. Some schools had of course teachers with honours in maths and physics, well able to teach physics, and it was common for talented pupils to take additional mathematics which really meant applied mathematics. Such pupils detected some of the inadequacies of the science teachers because they became on occasion more expert in problems in Newtonian mechanics than the science teacher.

Another important difference between the English and Scottish school-cum-university system, and one which largely persists to this day, was the fact that it required four years of study to do an Honours degree, at least one with physics as a major element. Often the pupil saved a year by leaving school following five years of instruction at secondary level. He entered university with a Scottish Higher Leaving Certificate and not with the GCE (General Certificate of Education) qualification. The school curriculum was often simpler than it tends to be nowadays. Virtually every pupil for the Leaving Certificate had to study English and mathematics and French. Those who took science as the fourth main subject of study generally pursued physics and chemistry; sometimes biology took the place of physics. A half Higher was offered in the subject rather badly labelled 'dynamics'.

Undergraduate University Provision

I have mentioned some of the features of the Scottish school scene because I have always felt that it was on the whole straightforward and generally efficient, the efficiency coming from the fact that the teachers were almost always, at least in Secondary schools, qualified with a good university degree and in addition instructed for a year at a Teachers Training College. Their standing in the community was high. There was virtually never any indiscipline in the schools. The Higher Leaving Certificate was a well-recognised qualification for entrance to a variety of professions while at the same time its possession guaranteed admission to a Scottish university. The minimum for its award in the 1920s and 1930s was two Highers and two Lowers. There was no fine division of grades within the Highers. Any young person with such a minimum entrance qualification that guaranteed that matriculation was possible could count on a Carnegie Trust grant to cover the very modest university fees. At that time the charges were usually in total £30 per annum.

In Glasgow University if a student was interested in physics as the principal science in which he could make a career he proceeded to take either an MA with Honours in mathematics and natural philosophy or a BSc with Honours in natural philosophy. Almost always at the end of the first year he was advised whether he should go into one of two streams and the less able of these streams finished at the end of a second year of study. The more able stream proceeded to four years in total to achieve an Honours qualification. The advice of staff on the division into Ordinary (pass) stream and Honours stream was almost invariably accepted.

The two departments of Natural Philosophy and Applied Physics generally had four supporting members of staff each and in 1935 for example they were Dr R A Houston, Mr C Cochrane, Dr W McFarlane and Dr J Thomson in the Natural Philosophy Department, and Dr George Green, Dr W Shearer, Dr George Allen and Dr R C Gray in Applied Physics. The natural philosophy staff taught all students of physics, in the case of the Honours class over a period of four years, and very often the first year natural philosophy class numbered 260–300; they were all accommodated in a big lecture theatre each day of five days of the week for one hour. The second year class would be approximately half that size. The junior Honours year numbered roughly 35 students and the senior Honours year about the same. Five Honours topics in physics (atomic physics, heat and thermodynamics, light, electricity and magnetism and dynamics) were offered and the third and fourth year students combined for four of them while dynamics was treated as a continuing subject for two years. In this way staff effort was used economically and speaking personally there seemed little disadvantage in being one of 70 or 80 students as against one of 35 or 40. The women students of physics were treated exactly the same way as the male students and generally were around 10 to 20 per cent of the total class.

The department was well housed in a building constructed soon after the end of Kelvin's long reign (in 1907). The father figure was Professor Taylor Jones, The Head of the Department, who influenced everything that occurred in the department. Very often he took the class himself, or at least maybe took the class half of the meetings of the session. This was one of the traditions of the Scottish universities of the period and perhaps a very interesting and important tradition. I know that some of the outstanding physicists from the English universities adopted the tradition willingly because they felt it was important in providing inspiration to students of the science.

At that time I was not very aware or informed about student-to-staff

Figure 16.1 The Natural Philosophy Department, University of Glasgow, completed in 1907.

ratios but would guess they were of the order of 15 to 1. Universities certainly did not expend cash extravagantly and quite a deal of the teaching was done with temporary members of staff appointed as Assistant Lecturers for three or so years. In the laboratories, which were usually very well-organised, a lot of the duties were assumed by student demonstrators and I recall doing those duties myself on at least one afternoon per week in each of two years. So the staff was compact and generally handling between 30 and 40 Honours students. During the 1930s Glasgow University had almost 5000 students in total, of whom between 30 and 40 per annum could be expected to complete the course and obtain a good Honours qualification in mathematics and natural philosophy or in natural philosophy. Looking back it seemed to be assumed by the staff that the number who were able to take a difficult Honours course was likely to be 40 or a little less when a total of 5000 were in the University, that is out of an enrolment of around 1200 per annum. In other words, 3 to 4 % of the University students were managing to achieve Honours in mathematics and physics or in physics only. I think the success of many of the graduates in physics stemmed from this firm concentration on a very small percentage of the available talent. My memory tells me the students worked conscientiously. There were roughly the same total number taking physics as a constituent part of their course, e.g. engineers, chemists, medicals, and dentists.

Structure of the Scottish Universities

The last point mentioned allows me to stress a feature of the Scottish universities of the inter-war years which was of considerable importance. The serious students did work hard and although on·paper the student-to-staff ratio of the University was high it was not high when it came to looking at the ratio in terms of output of Honours graduates. At that time there were four ancient universities in Scotland, three of them founded in the fifteenth century, St Andrews, Glasgow and Aberdeen, and Edinburgh founded in the following century. The people as a whole held the contribution of universities to the society in high esteem and indeed a professor could for those days be financially very well rewarded. I know that around 1930 a full professor might enjoy a salary of over £ 1400 per annum (plus other fees etc) and often be provided with a house at a nominal rent. There were of course relatively few professors and I recall that when I finished my Honours degree course in 1933 and spoke with the Head of Physics about doing research in his department, he asked me if I realised that there were only 13 Departments of Physics in the whole of the UK. For some reason, not obvious to me, he assumed that I wanted to be some day a Professor of Physics.

I should mention that for the past two centuries the four ancient universities had taken care to tend to certain technological aspects of their provision of science courses. This was to a large extent due to the influence of Professor John Anderson, Professor of Natural Philosophy at Glasgow University for many years up to 1796. He was the man who passionately advocated the pursuit of Applied Science but he was never narrow in his outlook. He befriended the young instrument maker James Watt and was an important influence on the career of Watt. He was a friend of Adam Smith, his contemporary and the distinguished author of *The Wealth of Nations*. He was a colleague of Joseph Black who discovered the importance of latent heat. He criticised rather violently the universities of the mid- and late eighteenth century for their lack of attention to what he believed was the most important challenge around, that is the advance of Applied Science, and on his death, following the terms of his famous Will, the Anderson Institution was launched in 1796. Its purpose was to pursue what we would describe as technological studies and such studies were offered not only to professional people but also to artisans. It was particularly stressed that all classes should be open to women. In many ways Anderson's work became far better known outwith Scotland and indeed outwith Britain than nearer home. Birkbeck was the second member of staff appointed to Anderson's Institution and he had a considerable influence in what became Birkbeck College. Anderson visited France and I have always wondered if his influence extended to the launching of the Ecole Polytechnique in 1797. Research on this matter could prove rewarding.

Commuting Students

However, to stop this digression and to return to features of the university scene and especially features bearing on instruction in physics I must remark on the tradition of the home-based student in many of the Scottish centres. Students travelled, usually rather efficiently, to their city university and this of course is not an uncommon feature of university education in many countries, although relatively rare in England. There are many important results of this habit, among them the fact that each of the Scottish universities had completely first-class students, the best of the talent of the neighbourhood. In the case of my own first university, Glasgow, it was supplied with the best students from a population of about two million in the greater city catchment area (commuting area). The excellence of students determined the quality of the work that was done by all. The best of them achieved a very good First Class degree and frequently also the top graduates went to do advanced work, usually at Oxford and Cambridge, but sometimes to other European and American universities. Quite often, some of them returned to appointments on the staff and so they were well informed in a world sense in mathematics and in physics and indeed in most sciences. In chemistry there was a sufficiently strong belief in their capabilities within Scotland for graduates to go much less often outwith Scotland.

One other obvious characteristic of the student in Scotland in the inter-war years was his relative lack of resources. He came from a family of very modest means and the incentive to do well in studies and in the jobs obtained through study was, to say the least, very considerable. For much the same reasons the student after graduation sought employment in a wide variety of spheres. More went into schoolteaching, but often the very able tried to avoid this. They were more likely to finish in university teaching itself but on the other hand many of the most able went to the Civil Service and a goodly fraction went into careers in industry. I can recall in my own time that of those who took First Class Honours and went on to do research, sometimes succeeding in having a PhD and sometimes failing, about half went to industry and to the Scientific Civil Service.

Research Capability

The capability of university departments of physics to do research was rather uneven. During my own time you had men like G P Thomson doing his most distinguished work on electron diffraction in Aberdeen. His early work on diffraction there won him the Nobel Prize. Professor Barkla in Edinburgh was recognised as an outstanding authority in x-ray research. In Glasgow the physics research was in the hands of Professor Edward Taylor Jones. Looking back on that period I have personally come to the conclusion that the members of staff who were reasonably active in research did not sufficiently closely supervise the research students. They knew that they were extremely able students, almost without exception with a good First Class Honours qualification, and from the word go they seemed to think they should be able to succeed in their research without much help or supervision as such. One result of this was that only about half of the research students succeeded in obtaining the PhD degree. I am sure that with a better introduction and better inculcation of research methodology the fraction succeeding could have been nearer 100%.

There was some opportunity to learn, not least in the student societies, but advanced lectures were not organised and I may say that I found better provision elsewhere, as when I went to Cambridge in 1937 and still better when I reached Berkeley, California, in 1944. The numbers in most of the Scottish University departments doing research made it rather less attractive to take the trouble to organise advanced courses, but I am convinced the lack of such instruction was a prime weakness. It had of course one very important outcome. The successful students who emerged from research study in physics were completely

Figure 16.2   Professor E Taylor Jones, the Head of the Department from 1926 to 1943.

self-reliant and in their future careers the reasonable provision of money and material was sufficient to guarantee they would achieve results.

In the physics department (Natural Philosophy and Applied Physics) of the nine or ten members of staff on average half were busy in their research and generally responsible for about ten research students. Undoubtedly the most inspirational of the lecturing staff so far as research students were concerned during the 1930s was John Thomson, a relatively young, industrious and dedicated research worker who played a large part in signals research in the Wills Research Laboratory at Bristol University during World War II and later became Director of the Royal Naval College at Greenwich. He appreciated the tremendous importance of the great discoveries in nuclear science around the late 1920s and early 1930s and, indeed, taught the subject with much enthusiasm.

Space was reasonably available but money was difficult, although not a major bottle-neck. I recall the Head of the Department, Taylor Jones, saying that he spent about £400 in cash per annum (this was not allowing for a fairly extensive workshop which backed up the researchers). In my own case I had no difficulty, such as I experienced in the Cavendish Laboratory, of getting platinum wire to make Geiger counters and no impediment was placed in my way in obtaining weekly, at a cost of ten shillings each, small radon capillary tubes containing 100 millicurie. Some of the cost of the research was borne by firms such as ICI and I am sure looking back that much more could have been obtained in the form of sponsorship than was the case in those inter-war years.

The Inspired Years

What I've said may give you a feeling that physics was humdrum from 1919 to 1939. It is true that it was taught in a rather humdrum way, without much publicity or media attention, but behind the scenes it was an amazing age of inspired work and this mattered greatly to all serious students. In my own case, and that of many others, the message seemed clear—we were participants in the wonderful age of inspired discovery. I recall seeing and hearing Rutherford and Moon on the neutron, and especially the slow neutron, when they attended the British Association Norwich Meeting in 1934. My resolve to make my career in nuclear physics was strong and it became unshakeable then. Assurance that physics was extremely important was present though it was difficult to be sure of personal involvement if you needed Carnegie grants, bursaries and paid work, preferably in physics, to be able to graduate with the requisite qualifications.

In the session 1929–30, I was Joseph Black medallist for first place in chemistry but chose to pursue physics and abandon chemistry for various reasons including the exciting prospects that discoveries in physics seemed to offer. After three more sessions of study of maths and physics, with equal weighting, I took first place in the final exams of 1933. I intended to do what was usually done—go to Cambridge on the Scholarship which I expected to get as first in the year. However, once in seven or so years it was only £120 per annum for three years that was available. I decided I had to stay in Glasgow and I asked if I could research in physics. The Head of the Department (there was a Professor James Gray in charge of Applied Physics, which was concerned chiefly with the service teaching of engineers, medical, dental and agricultural students) agreed to my proposal and invited me to proceed to show that beta-rays could be diffracted by thin films. For the session 1933–4 I studied part-time in astronomy and botany and was awarded BSc in 1934. Then full-time research effort for the next three sessions saw me publish on my own four papers, present a PhD thesis and graduate in early 1937. This success meant I obtained a Carnegie Fellowship to take me to join the Rutherford team at the Cavendish (£250 per annum changing to £400 plus £50 travel allowance a year later).

My passage to Cambridge was not truly typical of many of the students of the Scottish system of the time—it had been delayed but not frustrated and it demonstrated the belief I shared in the future of physics, a belief shared with almost all students of the period. The age was among the most remarkable of all time. The duality of matter, the development of quantum theory, wave mechanics, the discovery of the uncertainty principle, the new particles (like positron, neutron and meson), the artificial transmutation of atoms and artificial radioactivity opened up very many challenging vistas. So Cambridge in 1937, with the new Austin wing, was a most attractive place for physics. I felt ready to go there, and Glasgow, like other Scottish universities of the time, had fitted me to work successfully in research elsewhere. I had mastered the means of handling radioactive substances, especially the natural ones. I made rapid-action Geiger counters and I could tell Rutherford that 9 out of any 10 I made would operate well. In addition I knew how to make pulse amplifiers and was ready to be at home with the scalers of Dr W B Lewis (who succeeded Wynn-Williams). I know Rutherford wanted me to make Geiger counters perform well—he said that the Cavendish wasn't able to use them at all with success. My success came from liberal use of pure alcohol. (Trost explained the efficacy of heavy organic vapours later.)

While I had instructors of moderate learning and average research talent in Glasgow, at Cambridge I was among the world greats. In my own College, St John's, were people like John Cockcroft, Paul Dirac and Harold Jeffreys to name a few and elsewhere were Appleton, Rutherford himself, Dee, Feather, Lewis, Bretscher, Ratcliffe, Goldhaber, Hoyle and Alan Wilson. In the wings, but often present in discussions, were men like Allen and Shoenberg. Among those making their knowledge and experience available through visits were Blackett, Bragg, Darwin and Mott and Oliphant particularly. The research students themselves proved their qualities and had much to offer in creative thought. Perhaps the great concentration of genius was what brought success and maybe in Britain today we don't have just the few places where the truly outstanding bring out the best in each other.

The other attraction of Cambridge was the flow of truly stimulating

foreign physicists who were able to offer fresh challenge and insights—
men such as Bohr, Frisch, Lawrence, DuBridge, Casimir, Compton,
Joliot-Curie and Langmuir not to mention Lise Meitner. It was only in
Cambridge that one had such a series of stimulating visitors; they could
not give the corresponding time to less outstanding centres of research;
universities like Glasgow undoubtedly felt they were to some degree
'out in the cold'. I feel this must be said in defence of the departments
of physics of the Scottish universities—their size, geography and
budgets meant they faced real difficulties. To a large extent the years
after World War II have seen the problems of the inter-war years overcome. In Glasgow under Lord Kelvin marvellous results were accomplished but Kelvin was unique and of a unique age—he founded
industries of his own. His eminence was followed by a period of relative
decline and it was not an inconsiderable achievement that with comparatively major problems to face, physics in Scottish schools and
universities did reasonably well in 1919–39.

As I've said already, and as I should stress again, the student quality
was excellent, there was no spoon-feeding but fairly conscientious
instruction was the rule of the day and at the end of a course or of some
years in research the emerging physicist was, in my opinion, first and
foremost, self-reliant. They did fail to take the PhD at times, mainly
because the problem posed was *not* yet capable of solution, but they
emerged from the system ready to contribute effectively in government
science, in industrial research and in academic pursuits. Many good
examples could be quoted by way of illustration.

Perhaps there would have been still more good physicists if fission had
been discovered before early 1939. It was exactly the kind of discovery
with obvious practical applications that attracted a goodly fraction of
young Scottish physicists. I feel personally entitled to say this because
Rutherford asked me to write down a programme for my research at the
Cavendish. I had begun to use proportional counters and I felt I could
see heavy particles such as alpha-rays or protons when uranium was
bombarded with neutrons. I proposed work of that nature but could not
forecast I would observe fission. In fact I was with others finding the
observations on the transuranic elements puzzling and felt different
attacks, such as direct proportional counter observation, might help to
shed light on the phenomena. Rutherford placed me with P I Dee on
the 1.2 MV accelerator and happily my first experiment, chosen for a
variety of reasons of my own, gave results for proton capture by carbon
which were immediately of much value to Bethe in respect of his theory
of energy production in stars by virtue of the carbon cycle (carbon as
catalyst in making hydrogen into helium).

The Future

I would hope that we will do all we can to ensure we remain in the vanguard of teaching of physics in different ways as well as in the practice of physics. There is no reason to believe that retaining all that is best in the teaching of research by example (which is what characterised the inter-war years in my view) is in any way incompatible with the introduction of a much more advanced and formal instruction. I believe I was well aware during the pre-war years of the benefit to be derived from working for and with great physicists and I tried to create and avail myself of opportunities to do so. I came to learn much from a considerable number of Nobel Laureates, being in close touch with about ten of them. I do not wish to imply that Nobel Prize winners know and teach more—I mention them as illustrative of the kind of scientist who can often teach much in a telling fashion.

CHAPTER SEVENTEEN

BRISTOL AND MANCHESTER— THE YEARS 1931-9

Sir Bernard Lovell

I was a schoolboy in the 1920s when, mainly for the sake of the outing, I joined a party to hear A M Tyndall deliver a series of public lectures on the electric spark. In later years I learnt that Tyndall had delivered these as the Christmas Lectures at the Royal Institution. I do not know what inspired him to repeat these lectures in the magnificent new H H Wills Physical Laboratories of the University of Bristol. If he had not done so it is unlikely that I would have become a scientist. The brilliance of his lectures, the atmosphere created by the demonstrations and the splendid lecture theatre filled me with a desire to become one of his students.

When I eventually did so in 1931 I became one of a class of only six Honours physics students. Six years later I came to Manchester as an Assistant Lecturer and was alarmed to find that there were a dozen students in the Honours class. The size of the class must be one of the crucial differences distinguishing the inter-war period from today. I wonder how many universities today have physics classes of less than a hundred? It is not merely the size of the class in the lecture room that creates the difference but the consequential influence on the teacher–student relationship.

A social gulf exists today between staff and students of a type unknown in the inter-war years—and not merely because the size of the classes makes mutual extramural activities very difficult but also because of the age differential. The oldest of my teachers in Bristol in the early 1930s was A M Tyndall, the Director of the laboratory, and still in the full vigour of his research career. At that time he was in his early fifties and able to beat every one of his students on the tennis court. In the University cricket team I would often be bowling at one end with the senior lecturer in mathematics at the other. The point I am making is that our teachers were our near contemporaries. I believe that to be one of the most striking and saddest differences between today and 50 years ago. On 5 September 1985 the *New Scientist* published an article on the greying of British science. The figures for the inter-wars years are not given but the average age of researchers at the Cavendish increased from 37 in 1948 to 47 in 1983 and the proportion under 35 years of age has decreased from one half in 1948 to only 10 per cent in 1983. In the inter-war years there was a youthful community of interests between staff and students sadly lacking today.

Indeed, the coherence of the physics departments of the 1930s no longer exists. It is not only that the staff are no longer integrated with the students as they were in the inter-war years; the fact is that the members of the staff suffer lack of integration with one another. A few years ago whilst lecturing at one of those huge universities in the USA, I was taken to luncheon by the professors of physics, some of whom had to introduce themselves to one another even though they were not newcomers. We may not have reached that state but I am reminded that when Blackett succeeded W L Bragg as the Professor of Physics in Manchester in 1937 he was the only professor. Of course he soon remedied that by arranging for D R Hartree, the Professor of Applied Mathematics, to be reappointed to a Chair of Theoretical Physics. Today in the Manchester Physics Department there are 13 professors, three of whom are Professors of Theoretical Physics!

I think there can be little doubt that the students of the inter-war years were a privileged group compared with the students of today. I realised this most forcibly when, in preparation for this paper, I had a meeting with two dozen or so research students who had graduated during the last few years from a variety of British universities. Naturally, their experiences had varied widely but there was the regrettable common theme of the feeling that their teaching had been geared to get them through the examinations and that the examinations had been totally biased to the lecture courses to such an extent that it was not necessary to read textbooks. I am full of admiration for those who survive this type of disembodied production line to become the research scientists of today.

Until I referred to my own Honours physics examination papers of 1934 my instinctive feeling was that the physics courses today and the examinations for the Honours degree were far more difficult than 50 years ago. My conclusion is that this is not the case. The main difference is that in the 1930s our subject was simply 'physics'. Now there is a considerable range of options open to the undergraduate. This became inevitable after the war with the complex extension of physics into areas that simply did not exist in the 1930s—for example, the development of computer science, of electronics and microelectronics, particle physics, astronomy and astrophysics over the whole spectrum. However, in the cases I have examined, the structure of the courses has been

Figure 17.1   H H Wills Physics Laboratory, The University of Bristol, opened by Lord Rutherford in 1927. (Courtesy of the University of Bristol.)

cleverly adjusted so that whatever his choice the student must still understand 'physics' as we understood it in the inter-war period. The illustration of this is that, with the exception of theoretical physics, the option chosen by the undergraduate does not necessarily determine the subject of postgraduate research. This is most obviously the case in the astronomical sciences. Few institutions offer degrees in astronomy and a high percentage of those engaged in astronomical or astrophysical research have degrees in physics which may or may not have included an astrophysics or astronomical option. In other words, the teaching of the core of physics today is as good as it was 50 years ago in the sense that a good student is well educated in physics and in the methods of physics, notwithstanding the wide range of specialist options available.

Figure 17.2 The main entrance. The carvings in the spandrels over the door-way are representative examples of early and modern discoveries in experimental physics. Left: The dispersion of sunlight by a prism (Newton 1666). Right: the tracks of alpha particles from radium (CTR Wilson 1911). (Courtesy of The University of Bristol.)

If I compare my own 1934 final Part 2 Honours papers with those of Manchester physics examinations 50 years later in those areas where there is a degree of commonality, I find that the changes are minor. For example, in 1934 I had to answer this question: 'Discuss the spectra of hydrogen and of the alkali atoms on the basis of the wave mechanics, showing in particular why S terms have lower energy than P terms. Contrast the explanation given in Bohr's theory of orbits.' Fifty years later a Manchester student taking the atomic and molecular physics option had to answer an almost identical question: 'Explain why in a multielectron atom the energies of the single-particle levels depend both on the principal quantum number n and the orbital quantum number l. Why, for a given n does the s level lie below the p level?' In 1934, only two years after Chadwick's discovery, we had to 'Give a brief account of the experimental evidence on the existence and properties of the neutron.' I suspect that since the word neutron had not yet entered any textbook this was considerably harder to deal with than an equivalent question 50 years later in a Manchester nuclear physics option paper: 'The existence of neutrinos can be inferred without their being detected. Explain this statement and show how such indirect evidence can be used to find the mass and spin of the neutrino.' In the solid state option paper of the 1980s there are questions on specific heats and on paramagnetism and diamagnetism that could be interchanged without alteration with the physics papers of the 1930s.

I suspect that the initial years in most practical laboratories differ from

Figure 17.3   A research laboratory. (Courtesy of The University of Bristol.)

their predecessors of 50 years ago in the measuring equipment available, but scarcely at all in the experiments that have to be carried out. Whereas in the inter-war years there were lecture courses and textbooks on 'Properties of matter', dealing with various forms of pendulum, measurement of g and G and so on, this is now mostly covered in the practical classes. It is in the final year practical laboratory that the substantial changes have occurred, where the availability of more sophisticated equipment has made possible experimental work on many of the post-war developments in physics. But again, as in the examination questions, where there are areas of commonality the changes have been minor. For example, in the contemporary Manchester laboratory there is an experiment on the Zeeman effect with mercury arcs, using a Fabry–Perot etalon and photographic detection that is identical with my own 1934 experiment. On the other hand there are experiments on waveguides, radio interferometers, transmission lines and holograpy that would have had no meaning for physics students of the inter-war years.

The Teachers and Teaching Methods

In the inter-war period there was only one method of lecturing, and that was to use the blackboard with slides and practical demonstrations. My teachers of the 1930s may have carried notes with them but without exception they worked out the problems and equations as they wrote on the board. The invention of the viewgraph device and its widespread use today has introduced a new technique into teaching methods. Probably this has had the effect of making students more tolerant of the poor lecturer who writes out the entire lecture, or substantial notes for it, on the transparencies. The great advantage of the modern viewgraph is where the lecture theatre is so large that students at the back of the room may be unable to read the blackboard. The intelligent use of the device under such circumstances has certainly eased the task of teaching large classes and no doubt many of you will recall occasional examples where a lecturer has used the instrument to hold the attention of several hundred people under circumstances where a blackboard would have been invisible to the majority.

In spite of this important aid to teaching which, to some extent, may overcome the deficiencies of a lecturer, I suspect that many who occupy the lecture desk today would not have survived in the 1930s. Then it was possible to be sacked for inefficiency. Perhaps the present-day reversion to a form of sacking of poor staff will restore the competitive element of the inter-war years where an appointment to a university staff was a comparatively rare occurrence.

I wonder how many of today's students in the year 2035 AD will recall with admiration their teachers of today as I remember mine of the 1930s? There was, for example, Nevill Mott. For two years our physics had been almost entirely classical with the Professor of Theoretical Physics—Lennard Jones—covering the blackboard with the equations of classical electrodynamics. Then as we entered our final year Mott appeared. Even today if you open his small book published in 1930 and based on lectures he gave when on the Manchester staff, *An Outline of Wave Mechanics* (Mott 1930), you will see immediately the elegant simplicity of his treatment and realise the impact that his teaching had on students like myself. He was no exception amongst a distinguished staff whose names would be well known throughout the whole of the international community of physicists.

Of course, those of us who were undergraduates in the early 1930s were undoubtedly privileged to be young in those dramatic years of physics. I still have the vivid impression of R W Gurney or H W B Skinner excitedly coming into the lecture room with the newly arrived issue of *Nature* in their hands—the splitting of the atom, the discovery of the neutron, the positive electron, artificial radioactivity—we were taught physics at the very moment when it was being transformed. We had few teachers and so they remain in the memory: the youthful C F Powell—long before he turned his attention to cosmic rays and photographic emulsions—when he was still working on the mobility of ions; L C Jackson, who had just written the elegant monograph on low-temperature physics and had the complex hydrogen liquifier in the basement; W Sucksmith, the authority on gyromagnetism, whose research equipment was so sensitive that he could work only in the middle of the night when the Bristol trams were not running. Above all ruled Tyndall, ably assisted by the crystallographer S H Piper, a retired major, upright in stature, adviser and friend of any student who sought his help.

The Postgraduate Years

After I graduated in 1934 Tyndall obtained a DSIR maintenance grant to enable me to start research work for the PhD degree. The value of the grant was £120 per annum. I was allocated to E T S Appleyard as my supervisor to study the electrical conductivity of thin metallic films deposited in high vacua, particularly to find out why the resistivity of films with thicknesses of a few atomic layers differed from that of the bulk metal. I do not know why I was given this problem since, as far as I recall, it had no relation to other research work in the laboratory. In fact, the researches in Bristol at that time were diverse—it was an

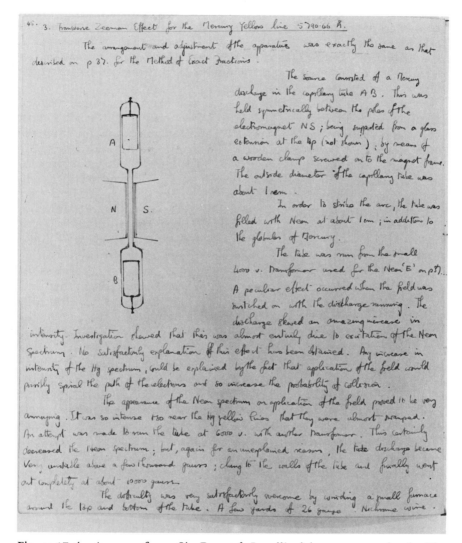

Figure 17.4 A page from Sir Bernard Lovell's laboratory notebook. The experiment was done between 3 November 1933 and 12 January 1934, his final undergraduate year. In the contemporary Manchester Laboratory there is an identical experiment for physics undergraduates.

epoch before the substantial concentration of research in one department demanded by expensive equipment. Tyndall and Powell were at work on the mobility of ions, Skinner on x-rays, Jackson and H London on low-temperature work, Sucksmith and H H Potter on magnetism and Piper on x-ray crystallography. W R Harper and his wife seemed to be engaged on some obscure high-voltage research, V C Cosslett on electron diffraction and late on any night C R Burch could be seen bent over and grinding away at his lenses.

If there was a common theme it was the need for a highly skilled glass-blower. At that time J H Burrow was one of the world's most skilled glass-blowers, able to make complex glass equipment from the newly developed Pyrex glass as though manipulating Plasticine. To a considerable extent Burrow controlled the progress of the various researchers since nearly every piece of research equipment needed his attention. It was important to establish good relations with him and since my own high-vacuum equipment needed his extreme skill and continuous attention, it was fortunate that I became his friend at an early stage.

Mott ruled over a formidable array of theorists—Heitler, H Jones, Zener, Bethe, Gurney were either there permanently or were visiting fellows at this period and K Fuchs (the post-war atomic traitor) was my neighbour. Any young person who worked in the laboratory at that time must have nostalgic memories, as I do, of the help and advice readily available on almost any experimental or theoretical topic and of the superb accommodation which we did not appreciate until we moved elsewhere.

My own reluctant move came in 1936. Favoured by Burrow, helped by Appleyard and with more than a fair share of good fortune with the delicate equipment, I had finished my allocated research programme. Tyndall summoned me and announced that it was time I moved 'to get more competition'. He said that Blackett was looking for a young man at Birkbeck but that it would also be advisable to apply for an Assistant Lectureship in Manchester. My ardent desire to work with Blackett was not to be satisfied so easily and in the autumn of 1936 I found myself a somewhat unwilling member of W L Bragg's Manchester staff. The research in the department was far more concentrated than in Bristol and x-ray crystallography dominated the scene. J M Nuttall, E C Scott-Dickson and R W James were teaching but I do not remember whether they were still engaged in research. S Tolansky ran his optical interferometer research more or less as a closed shop in the basement. The people I recall as Bragg's chief researchers were Lipson, Beevers and W H Taylor. The steward, William Kay, of the Rutherford epoch, ruled the laboratory.

I tried, but failed absolutely, to interest myself in Bragg's research and made the bad mistake of trying to restart my thin film work in a place with no facilities and with only a poor quality commercial glass-blower several streets away. Eventually, with the agreement of both Bragg and Tyndall, I spent a long vacation in Bristol and, helped by Burrow, completed another set of measurements. Soon, my Manchester interest was gripped by D R Hartree's mechanical differential analyser built in a part of the basement. This exquisite piece of machinery was marvellously engineered and Hartree used it with Arthur Porter (later of Ferranti and Toronto) to solve many complex equations. Whilst helping Hartree with this work I encountered F C Williams who was a member of the Electrotechnics Department, which was joined to the Physics Department by a dark and grimy corridor. Williams, even at that stage, was interested in the work of the machine. In order to supply this machine with information in the form of a functional relation between variables it was necessary to keep a pointer on a graph on an input table. The x-coordinate screw was driven by the machine but the y-coordinate screw had to be operated by hand to keep the pointer on the curve. Williams developed a photoelectric device for this purpose and in partnership with Blackett, after he arrived in Manchester, this was still further refined to produce an automatic device that followed the curve far more accurately than could be done by hand (Blackett and Williams 1939). In the light of the electronic and technical developments of that period this was a remarkable achievement and no doubt was one of the initial stimuli that led to Williams' important post-war computer developments.

In the autumn of 1937, a year after I had arrived in Manchester, a most spectacular transformation occurred in the Physics Department. W L Bragg left Manchester to become the Director of the National Physical Laboratory (he succeeded Rutherford as Cavendish Professor a year later). Bragg was succeeded by Blackett as the Langworthy Professor of Physics (and thus my own great desire to work with Blackett was fulfilled by this twist of fate). I suspect that this is one of the last examples where a new Director of a university physics laboratory so completely brought his own discipline with him. Even at that time Blackett's large cosmic ray magnet was a substantial piece of equipment and another large room between the department and the electrotechnics empire was commandeered to house it. Within a few months all crystallographic personnel had disappeared and a quarter century of tradition was swept aside by moving Kay from his quarters behind the lecture room to a ground-floor room near the entrance; the dark brown of the walls was painted out; a departmental library was started and the workshop was moved from the basement slums to a more worthy ground-floor site. Of Bragg's staff only Tolansky survived to carry on his existing research. Nuttall and Scott-Dickson were left to carry the brunt of the teaching load and Hartree's appointment was changed to

Professor of Theoretical Physics. Blackett inherited G D Rochester and myself from Bragg's staff and brought with him from Birkbeck J G Wilson, L Jánossy and, subsequently, H J J Braddick.

However, the permanent staff were small fry compared with the eminent physicists who flocked to the department (some as refugees from Europe). We soon became well acquainted with Auger, Bhabha, Carmichael, Cosyns, Dymond, Occhialini, Duperier, Heisenberg, Heitler, Rossi, Wataghin, E J Williams and many other famous scientists of the inter-war years. I have given elsewhere a detailed account of the work in Blackett's laboratory during those years and after the war (Lovell 1975) and here I make only two further comments. Blackett was frequently absent in London and only much later did we learn that he was so vitally engaged on the Tizard Committee and with the early development of radar. Those of us who were young viewed his returns to the department with some apprehension. He would instantly find us, remove a card from his pocket and demand immediate action on many points he had noted during the train journey. Blackett was a superb craftsman and he assumed that we would also posses his ability, whether as a glass-blower to make a Geiger counter or as an engineer to design and manufacture a new electromagnet.

My second comment concerns the memory of a weekend conference and of a classic dispute between Blackett, Bhabha and Heisenberg. I should mention that Blackett had little patience with weekends. His view was that a change of scene on Sunday was adequate. That meant six days in the laboratory and the change of scene was an arduous walk on the Pennines with Blackett and his wife during which any scientific or other topics omitted during the week were covered. This routine would be varied as often as possible by the organisation of a conference extending over the Saturday and Sunday. Blackett nearly always dominated these meetings but on the occasion to which I refer he was defeated on a fundamental point in physics.

The issue concerned the nature of the penetrating component of cosmic rays. In the last year of his work at Birkbeck, Blackett, with J G Wilson, studied the energy loss of cosmic ray particles incident on a metal plate in the cloud chamber. They concluded that the quantum theory of radiation must fail at high energies. It was a curious situation because Blackett knew about the Bhabha–Heitler cascade theory of shower production (Bhabha and Heitler 1937). In fact, the controversial Blackett–Wilson paper (Blackett and Wilson 1937) was communicated to the Royal Society three weeks after the *publication* of the Bhabha–Heitler paper. Further, the important paper by Bethe and Heitler (Bethe and Heitler 1934) on the radiation loss of high-energy electrons had been published in 1934, and Neddermeyer and Anderson had already concluded that the penetrating component of cosmic rays at sea-level must be particles heavier than electrons (Neddermeyer and Anderson 1937). The confrontation with Bhabha and Heisenberg occurred a few months after Blackett had arrived in Manchester. Like the other junior members present I listened spellbound throughout the Saturday as Blackett stubbornly argued his point that the quantum theory failed at high energies. When we reassembled on the Sunday morning Blackett had lost confidence and slowly began to concede that the penetrating component was a particle heavier than an electron and that the quantum theory of radiation did not fail at high energies. By the summer of 1938 he had completely rationalised his cloud chamber results and in August, in an introductory address to a Section A symposium of the British Association, he gave a concise explanation (Blackett 1938). After explaining how an energetic electron produced a cascade shower according to the Bhabha–Heitler theory, he said 'Once the validity of the quantum theory for electrons with energies of $10^{10}-10^{11}$ eV had been established, it became certain that the penetrating rays, which are in a great majority at sea-level, must consist of a new type of particle with a mass intermediate between that of an electron and that of a proton.'

Today with the rapid dissemination of important scientific results it is hard to remember that in the inter-war years results of critical importance often travelled slowly. I do not know whether Blackett was in touch with the experiments on fission, but on a Saturday afternoon in January 1939 I was in the laboratory discussing some of my cosmic ray results with him as we walked up the stairs of the Schuster Laboratory to his office. Those of you who remember that building will know that the stairs reverse direction at the halfway mark. As we reached that landing a boy carrying a cable ran into the building and handed it to Blackett. It was from a group of American scientists. At a meeting of the American Physical Society Bohr had described the work of Hahn and Strassmann. The Meitner–Frisch explanation of these results was dated 16 January 1939 and had been communicated to *Nature*. The cable urged Blackett to use his influence to stop the publication of these results. He handed me the cable. 'What will you do?' Blackett replied 'I cannot do that' and we continued to discuss cosmic rays.

The Changing Nature of Research

As a final comment I would like to make a few remarks about the changes in the nature of scientific research. In the inter-war years research was very much a personal affair. Even in laboratories such as Manchester, where one topic was dominant (x-ray crystallography and then cosmic rays in the years of which I write), the research worker had his own equipment, often designed and constructed by himself. It was unusual for more than two people to collaborate in the same experiment using one piece of equipment. Nearly always the scientist operated the equipment and moreover tended to guard his results with some jealousy until they were published.

Perhaps in some aspects of physics this situation still applies, but in others the advent of large and expensive machines has completely altered the attitude of student and research worker. For example, neither in high-energy physics nor in astronomy can one have the intimate contact with the machines that existed in the inter-war years. The large teams of ancillary staff required to maintain and operate these huge pieces of research equipment are a post-war phenomenon. Very little front-line astronomical research is now carried out with the astronomer in the prime focus cage of the telescope . Nearly always, he is in a computerised laboratory, not even able to see the telescope he is using. It is now possible for a student to carry out research for a higher degree without any real acquaintance with the equipment that has made his measurements. Very often skills in computer operation or software development are the critical factors in successful research even though the topic of research has no relation to computer science.

We are too immersed in this phase to judge whether the ultimate effects on the progress of science will be beneficial. The students do not seem unhappy with the conditions. They point out that whereas they spend months on software development we had similar lengthy periods of unproductive effort struggling with the electronics or other idiosyncrasies of our elementary machines. It is a valid point of view; nevertheless I am glad that I belong to an age where we were taught to use lathes and soldering irons.

References

Bethe H and Heitler W 1934 *Proc. R. Soc.* A **146** 83
Bhabha H and Heitler W 1937 *Proc. R. Soc.* A **159** 432
Blackett P M S 1938 *Nature* **142** 692
Blackett P M S and Williams F C 1939 *Proc. Camb. Phil. Soc.* **35** 494
Blackett P M S and Wilson J G 1937 *Proc. R. Soc.* A **160** 304
Lovell B 1975 *Biogr. Mem. R. Soc.* **21** 1
Mott N F 1930 *An Outline of Wave Mechanics* (Cambridge: Cambridge University Press)
Neddermeyer S H and Anderson C D 1937 *Phys. Rev.* **51** 884

CHAPTER EIGHTEEN

SOME THOUGHTS ON PHYSICS COURSES IN CAMBRIDGE: 1931-7

W E Burcham

A Little Mathematics (and a Little Physics) 1931–2

When I arrived as a freshman at Trinity Hall in October 1931 I was assigned to a personal tutor and to a director of studies with whom I discussed my interests. He recommended me to approach the Natural Sciences Tripos Part II Physics by taking the Mathematical Tripos Part I at the end of my first year so that I could spend two years on physics. I was very happy with this proposal although the escape from the excellent multidisciplinary Natural Sciences Tripos Part I was probably very bad for me educationally. The mathematics–physics combination was in fact not very different from what is offered in the average physics department today.

My director of studies sent me to a mathematics supervisor from another college and he told me that lectures were listed in the *Cambridge University Reporter* and that I had better go to statics and dynamics, algebra and trigonometry, geometry and the applied subjects geometrical optics, electricity and magnetism and hydrostatics. At no time did I see a syllabus for the Tripos examination and such knowledge could only be gleaned by looking at past examination questions. Some of these were given out by the lecturers and answers to them would be marked if they were sent in, although there was no obligation to do so. Tripos questions were also set and discussed by my supervisor at our weekly meetings, with one other student. There were no obvious duplicating facilities for circulation of information or questions and at lectures all material was written on a blackboard. Success in Mathematics Part I depended mainly on the acquisition through practice of certain basic skills in puzzle-solving and was therefore very largely a matter of individual effort. Textbooks did not figure prominently in the lectures, though plenty were available in Cambridge libraries.

The mathematics lectures occupied only about nine hours a week and left plenty of time for other things so I attended in addition the physics lectures on electricity and magnetism given by C D Ellis in the Cavendish Laboratory. These lectures were superb by my standards although experimental demonstrations were few and far between. I also went to Ellis's practical class in one of the dingy annexes of the Cavendish and much enjoyed it since it brought me into contact with Ellis himself and led to more than a few words of encouragement. The laboratory was open on three mornings or afternoons a week and the list of experiments included comparison of resistances, the hysteresis cycle, impedance, triode characteristics and the power factor of a condenser. A brief manuscript instruction existed for each and a record was kept of student completion of each exercise, although as far as I know no report went back to my director of studies in College since this course was just an 'extra' for me.

During the short Easter term, when the mathematics lectures were mainly revision, I saw advertised in the *Reporter* a course on quantum theory to be given by N F Mott. I had no right to go to any such course but I did so, as was possible in Cambridge, and I found it new and exciting, because the subject was only just working its way into the physics course. In the summer of 1932 I kept the first of a sequence of Long Vacation terms. I have still to find a more pleasant way of studying, partly I suppose because examinations seemed remote but mainly I believe because of the sheer charm of summertime in pre-war Cambridge. Practical demonstrations, as they were quaintly described, were provided in science subjects and I attended G F C Searle's mechanics, heat and optics class.

Searle, who was already a legend, had established in the Cavendish a highly individual style of teaching which is enshrined in his books on optics, harmonic motion and elasticity. It was a style which gave supreme credit to accurate measurement and which expressed results to a large number of significant figures. Not many of us achieved the standards set by Searle, either in performing experiments or in recording results tidily, and most of us attracted attention and criticism which could be devastating to a raw student. Before the end of term, however, we came to admire his skill and to respect the warmth of personality that lay beneath a somewhat forbidding exterior. In Searle's class the experiments through which I worked included cardinal points of a thick lens, circular fringes, viscosity of water, g by rigid pendulum and the thermal conductivity of copper. Nobody looked very carefully at my lab book and my accounts now seem very naive, particularly in the matter of errors. All calculations in this class, as in Ellis's laboratory, were done with log tables or slide-rules although Searle, as Philip Moon reminds me, did not approve of the latter.

Figure 18.1   G F C Searle in the Optics Laboratory. (Courtesy of the Cavendish Laboratory.)

More Physics (but Less Mathematics) 1932–4

In 1932 the Cavendish Laboratory under Rutherford was at the height of its fame as a centre for nuclear physics—that very year had seen the discovery of the neutron by Chadwick and of artificial disintegration using accelerated ions by Cockcroft and Walton.† Exciting things were happening on every hand but Rutherford expected staff members to do their full share of University and College teaching. My own director of studies sent me for physics supervision to P M S Blackett, who, unknown to me, was at that very time establishing the photoproduction of electron–positron pairs. This later contributed to his being awarded the Nobel Prize.

Blackett was a supervisor who nearly always terrified me but who taught me for an hour each week both conscientiously and brilliantly for a whole year. He told me not to attend the lectures on heat given by Searle since I could read all that up in books, but I was to go to his own optics course, to the course given by Ratcliffe on electric oscillations and waves, to Mott's 'Physics and the Quantum Theory' lectures and to Rutherford's 'Constitution of Matter'. I have notes of most of these and recollections of them all, especially of Blackett's in which the lecturer used not a single note but gave an outstandingly clear and authoritative account of the principles of physical optics, an account which I used for my own purposes for nearly fifty years. None of the lectures included any hand-outs or question papers and very few, except Rutherford's and Ratcliffe's, provided experimental demonstrations. No doubt the lack of a cathode-ray oscillograph in the lecture preparation room restricted this type of activity. There were usually no visual aids other than the blackboard, though Rutherford, who could command technical support, sometimes used a few $3'' \times 3''$ slides.

In my final year the total number of students was between 20 and 30, including one lady who courageously often arrived late for lectures. Some of these were held in the main Cavendish lecture theatre, reputedly designed by Maxwell, in which an exceptional degree of discomfort was offered by the seating. Others were accommodated elsewhere, less historically but more comfortably. Lectures were given after tea as well as in the morning, and on Saturdays as well as Monday to Friday, sometimes as late as noon on that day. In addition to the physics courses I went also to some mathematics lectures on differential equations and I arranged through college to have some personal supervision in mathematical methods, although Blackett frequently advised me not to do too much mathematics at the expense of the physics background.

Blackett also had charge of the Part II Physics practical laboratory, which had modest equipment but high standards. We were given only minimal information about experiments (contained in a well-known

---

†An excellent account of all this and much more may be read in the book *Cambridge Physics in the Thirties*, edited by J Hendry (Bristol: Adam Hilger, 1984).

grey book) and we often had to make much of the apparatus ourselves (see figure 18.2). For most of us, I think, the Part II class was a chastening experience, but it was very important because it taught us about the real world of physics. It also brought us together and helped to create a sense of belonging to the Laboratory as well as to one's own College.

I covered all the normal Part II Physics course in my second

MICHAELMAS TERM 1932

Variation of Surface Tension of Water with Temperature   Oct 1932

Apparatus

A length of glass tubing is heated near one end and is drawn out at this point into a capillary about 10 cms long and 1mm in diameter. The capillary

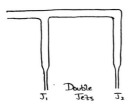

is then divided at the centre to form two identical circular jets, the shorter of which is sealed to the stem of the other in the form of a T-piece. The other jet is then bent over until the two jets are

Double Jets J₁ J₂

parallel. The joint & the bend are allowed to cool gradually, so as to prevent fractures and when cool the apparatus is washed with chromic acid.

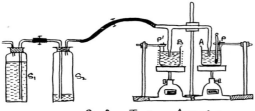

Surface Tension Apparatus

An apparatus of the form shown is then set up. The jets are supported in a clamp so as to be fixed vertically, and dip under the surface of water contained in beakers A & B, which stand on

Figure 18.2 This illustration is taken from Professor Burcham's 'written-up' practical book and refers to an experiment that most Part II students will remember.

undergraduate year and spent my final year on consolidation of my personal notes and on attending lectures culled without anybody's advice from the pages of the *Reporter*. These included 'Combination of Observations', 'Quantum Theory of Spectra', 'Physics of the Upper Atmosphere', 'Dynamical Theory of Gases', 'Classical Electron Theory' and 'Band Spectra'. Additionally, because it was Cambridge, there were short specialised courses by people such as J J Thomson, F W Aston, C T R Wilson and P Kapitza and I went to as many of these as I could. In the end, by the Easter term 1934 I had what I deemed adequate notebooks covering the four main papers of the Tripos examination. I had used textbooks as well as lectures in compiling these notes and I felt that I had some understanding of most of the main branches of physics as they stood in 1934, crystal physics being perhaps the most notable exception. In 1934 of course physics was much more compact and it was still possible for a university teacher to know nearly *all* the physics that a student needed for his final examination.

Comparison of Student Physics Teaching: 1934 and 1984

I think that the main difference between Cambridge teaching of the 1930s in Part II Physics and the comparable teaching today is in the control of student progress. The Cambridge course did not appear to be planned in much detail and suffered because lectures were given by the University and supervisions by the Colleges. Although the undergraduate did not have to work harder he had to work differently, searching for reference material and judging for himself whether a particular topic was interesting, important or just likely to appear in the examination. I have tried to compare the actual content of the courses and a few notes are shown in table 18.1. Obviously much new physics has appeared since 1934 and this has led to a widespread use of the option system which was not then necessary. Most of the 1934 Cambridge physics course is in fact covered in Birmingham by the end of the second year and the third year presents the options and the basic physics advances of the last fifty years. In 1934 we did spend a lot of time in learning about details of actual experiments and equipment and this was perhaps because theoretical physics had then not quite emerged as the powerful discipline that it now is. The material of subjects like condensed matter was spread over a variety of traditional courses such as heat, electricity and magnetism and properties of matter. On the other hand the classical mathematical physics of thermodynamics and electricity and magnetism was taught as well as it now is. Quantum mechanics for physicists was essentially Schrödinger's wave mechanics. The 1934 Tripos examination included an essay and a practical test, but

Table 18.1   Undergraduate physics: 1934 and 1984 compared.

Birmingham 1984	*Cambridge 1934*
Units MKS	CGS
Quantum mechanics	Essentially Schrödinger's wave mechanics contrasted with old quantum theory. No operator formalism.
Electricity and magnetism	Classical theory well-taught, not much difference. Thermionic valves important.
Thermal physics	Again classical theory well-taught. Much attention to individual experiments.
Optics	Obviously no holography or lasers. Not much on coherence, but general wave theory at about same level.
Solid state	Current topics were scattered over the courses in heat, electricity and properties of matter. No coordinating quantum mechanical theory. No semiconductors and little on superfluids.
Nuclear structure and elementary particles	Really only α-particle experiments and cosmic rays. Most of the subject still to come.

no general problem paper of the sort that is now used by many universities.

Research 1934–7

The award of a DSIR research studentship necessitated not only an adequate performance in the degree examination but also a strong recommendation from the Laboratory, which for this purpose was the staff of the Part II Physics practical class. In my case I think that the recommendation was probably made by Rutherford on the advice of P I Dee, who had taken over the class from Blackett and who had looked at some of my work during the year 1933–4. The recommendation was successful and the studentship gave me adequate financial support for two years from October 1934.

I was keen to get started so I kept the Long Vacation term of 1934, as did most of the new research students, and after a few days and some waiting about I saw both Chadwick and Rutherford. They asked me what I wanted to do and listened to ideas that I had about working with Cockcroft but rightly deemed that this was too ambitious. In the end it was decided that I might like to reconstruct a derelict piece of high-tension equipment and use it to find the best form of discharge tube for producing high positive ion currents. To start with, however, I could well spend the Long Vacation term in measuring the speed of some new diffusion pumps that had been set up in the technician's room in the High Voltage Laboratory. Chadwick was to be my research supervisor, but for the diffusion pump work I could get advice from Cockcroft and from Dee. This I certainly received, together with much help from the technician Birtwhistle, but the diffusion pumps never worked for me, probably because of insufficiently low backing pressure. I began already to see that passing examinations does not necessarily ensure immediate success in real, live physics.

Towards the end of 1934 or early in 1935 it became known that Chadwick was to leave Cambridge for Liverpool. By then I was working on the rehabilitation of the small high-tension equipment with B C Browne, another research student, and with him I was transferred to M L E Oliphant, who was to become Assistant Director of Research in succession to Chadwick and in partnership with Ellis. Oliphant asked us to continue instrumental development but to concentrate on the construction of a high-tension mercury vapour rectifier for accelerator physics. Later he also asked us to take over some work that had just started in the laboratory on photographic emulsion detectors of nuclear particles. Neither of these seemed to me to be a very attractive alternative to work on disintegration experiments and I did not realise the latent power of the photographic technique, which later brought the Nobel Prize to C F Powell for the discovery of the pion. Nor did I have any good knowledge of the interesting things that needed doing in nuclear physics—the theory of the subject had not then been formulated by Bethe (and others) and there were no graduate lectures to cover the subject systematically in depth. Rutherford did not encourage theoretical work in the Cavendish, but he did not forbid it and when Maurice Goldhaber joined the Laboratory some of us began to think more closely about what we were doing. I am grateful to him for a host of useful ideas.

For about a year Browne and I worked on rectifiers and on the nuclear emulsion technique and accounts of what we did, which was a very modest achievement indeed, found their way into my PhD thesis. Oliphant was busy at the time with plans for the proposed new high-tension equipment of the laboratory and gave us encouragement and ideas rather than detailed supervision. We did not have anything approximating to a well-defined research programme of the sort that is now expected by Research Councils. Somehow this did not matter because there were exciting things and people all round us and the PhD was less important in Rutherford's opinion, I think, than getting new results. Most of us were of course registered for the degree in the Faculty of Physics and Chemistry at the end of our first year of research and it was that fact that perhaps led to a redirection of our research.

My fellow student Browne had been quickly spotted by Rutherford as a very able young man and he was invited to join the Professor's own research group, in which the main practical thrust was provided by Oliphant, with able help from Albert Kempton and Reinet Maasdorp.† This group, which had discovered the deuteron–deuteron reactions, was in one sense complementary to that of Cockcroft and Walton and in another sense competitive with it. Walton, however, had left in 1934 and Cockcroft was increasingly involved in the Mond Laboratory and in the design of the proposed Cavendish cyclotron, leaving the ongoing programme of disintegration work using counters to W B Lewis. The Cockcroft–Walton equipment was indeed being used by Dee and C W Gilbert for track chamber work, but they could not take all the available time and to my great pleasure I was asked by Oliphant to transfer to the counter work in the High-tension Laboratory.

Lewis was as much interested in instruments as in nuclear reactions, and he saw both as tools necessary for establishing nuclear masses. He planned a programme of accurate range measurements on disintegration particles, but before we actually got started the whole Laboratory was excited by a paper from Shankland in the USA questioning the simultaneity of the production of a scattered photon and a recoil electron in the Compton effect as verified by Bothe and Geiger. Such a conclusion denied the conservation of energy in individual events, which was a matter that had been seriously discussed by Bohr, Kramers and Slater. Because of the profound implications that Shankland's result would have for the new quantum mechanics, Dee in particular felt that the result must be checked and that with the availability of Lewis's electronic skills, we were the group to do it. I am afraid that I regarded this as a somewhat unwelcome interruption, but everybody else was keen and together we created an x-ray scattering experiment with home-made Geiger counter detection of the photon and recoil electron. After a good many troubles with the counters, we were able to establish a reliable coincidence counting rate which showed that Shankland's results were unlikely to be valid. A short paper reporting these measurements and an even shorter one on the behaviour of newly-made Geiger counters, both in the *Proceedings of the Cambridge Philosophical Society* for 1936, were my first publications. I was able to

---

†Miss Maasdorp (Mrs J H Fremlin) was the only girl research student whom I remember during the academic years 1934–7, although from 1937 onwards numbers began to increase. The Cavendish staff included Miss A C Davies (Mrs Horton) whose sympathetic appraisal of poorly-reported experiments made her popular with students in the Part II class.

use the Compton experiment in my thesis and I only mention this episode in order to emphasise the overriding priority that was always given to important physics in the Cavendish.

In 1936 the University received a very substantial benefaction from Sir Herbert Austin, following an appeal on behalf of the Cavendish Laboratory written by Sir Arthur Eddington. This immediately turned the possibility of a new high-tension laboratory into something really achievable and it accelerated the end of the Cockcroft–Walton equipment with which I was working. It also meant the beginning of a new undertaking for me personally because in July 1936 Rutherford, no doubt advised by Oliphant and Dee, asked me if I would help to get the new laboratory working. Not unnaturally I was delighted with this distinction and I began to feel less worried than I had been previously about my PhD thesis, which finally contained three main and unrelated topics. It was in fact accepted in this form by Rutherford and Dee as my examiners in the early summer of 1937.

My new duty in the laboratory also helped me out of a financial difficulty that beset many research students in the 1930s. Then as now the government funding authority (DSIR) was not interested in the PhD degree as such, but only in training in research, for which a two-year grant was deemed adequate. We therefore had to start looking round for additional money towards the end of our second year, with the prospect that if unlucky, we might have no more than fees from

Figure 18.3 The Garage, The Cavendish Laboratory, 1937. The non-nuclear physics experiments were housed here. (Courtesy of the Cavendish Laboratory.)

demonstrating in undergraduate practical classes.† In my own case I was lucky because, probably on the recommendation of Rutherford, I was awarded a studentship of the Goldsmith's Company. Then later in 1936 I was advised by my College tutor to apply for the Stokes Studentship at Pembroke College and this also I was awarded, again probably because of recommendations from the Laboratory. The latter award enabled me to raise my standard of living in my new College during the completion of my thesis in 1937 and for the two years that intervened before the beginning of World War II.

Comparison of PhD Courses 1934 and 1984

As with the first degree, I think that the most important difference between the PhD course in Cambridge in 1934 and that in say Birmingham fifty years later is in the control of student progress. The degree had been made available in Cambridge in about 1920 and by 1934 research students were expected to register for that degree, or for the less demanding MSc, after a year's research. It was understood in the Cavendish that only exceptionally would a PhD degree be completed in less than 3 years altogether and it was expected that students would in this time be able to put together enough material for an examinable thesis. Rutherford always gave great care to the choice of projects for research but his interest was in advancing the understanding of physics and not primarily in providing thesis material. It was not felt that students needed any formal instruction as part of their PhD programme, although it was conceded that they should continually refurbish their general physics, an undertaking that was helped by demonstrating in the practical laboratories. In 1934 there was no predoctoral test or examination and students had little opportunity of presenting their work at seminars or technical conferences. There was no external examiner at the final PhD assessment—often the pattern was Rutherford himself and a staff member who knew the student's work and could be assumed to have read the thesis.

Today we are familiar with the large well-developed research facilities that are available for PhD programmes. But fortunately we still find the smaller, more original, less certain types of project like those of the Cavendish fifty years ago, in which there is an element of risk. It is a tribute to the flexibility of the PhD degree structure that despite much criticism it has withstood the test of time and is now as much in demand

---

†I have a notebook which shows that I demonstrated in the Part II class during 1936–7. Among the students that year were two young Americans, C Kittel and N F Ramsey.

Table 18.2   Postgraduate (PhD) physics: 1934 and 1984 compared.

Birmingham 1984	*Cambridge 1934*
Duration 3(+) years	3(+) years
Research Studentships 3 years	2 years
Postgraduate lectures given	No formal lectures
PhD mid-course assessment	None
Research group seminars frequent	Groups too small, but regular Cavendish Physical Society meetings
Relevant conferences well supported	Little opportunity
Demonstrating normal	Demonstrating encouraged
Examiners include external	No external examiners

as ever. I have gathered together in table 18.2 some of the points mentioned above for ease of comparison between 1934 and 1984.

APPENDIX ONE

NOTES ON THE AUTHORS

Professor T E Allibone CBE, FRS, FEng, FInstP (b. 1903)
Central School, Sheffield; University of Sheffield (Linley Scholar)
(1921–6) BSc, PhD (Metallurgy); Gonville and Caius, Cambridge
(Wollaston Scholar, 1851 Exhibitioner) PhD (1929). Director, High
Voltage Laboratory, Metropolitan-Vickers Electrical Company, Man-
chester (1930–46). Member, British Mission on Atomic Energy to
Berkeley and Oak Ridge (1944–5). Director, AEI Research Laboratory,
Aldermaston (1946–63) and AEI (Woolwich) Ltd (1948–63). Chief
Scientist, Central Electricity Generating Board (1963–70). Now Robert
Kitchin Research Professor, City University, London. Emeritus Pro-
fessor, University of Leeds.
Publications include: 1976 *Royal Society and its Dining Clubs* (Oxford:
Pergamon).
1983 (With G Hartcup) *Cockcroft and the Atom*
(Bristol: Adam Hilger)

Professor H A Brück CBE, FRSE, MRIA (b. 1905)
Augusta Gymnasium, Charlottenburg; Universities of Bonn, Kiel,
Munich and Cambridge. Astronomer, Potsdam Observatory (1928).
Lecturer, University of Berlin (1935). Research Associate, Vatican
Observatory (1936). Assistant Observer, Solar Physics Observatory,
Cambridge (1937). John Couch Adams Astronomer, Cambridge
(1943). Assistant Director, Cambridge Observatory (1946). Director,
Dunsink Observatory, and Professor of Astronomy, Dublin Institute of
Advanced Studies (1947–57). Astronomer Royal, Scotland, and Regius
Professor of Astronomy, Edinburgh (1957–75). Now Professor
Emeritus.

Publications include: 1983 *Story of Astronomy in Edinburgh from its beginnings until 1975* (Edinburgh: Edinburgh University Press)
1982 ed. *Astrophysical Cosmology*

Professor W E Burcham CBE, FRS, FInstP (b. 1913)
City of Norwich School; Trinity Hall, Cambridge (1931–7) BSc, PhD; Stokes Student, Pembroke College, Cambridge (1937–9). Scientific Officer, Ministry of Supply and Directorate of Atomic Energy (1939–44). Lecturer, Cambridge (1946–51). Oliver Lodge Chair of Physics, University of Birmingham (1957–80).
Publications include: 1979 *Elements of Nuclear Physics* (London: Longman)

Professor Sir Samuel Curran FRS, FRSE, FEng, FInstP (b. 1912)
University of Glasgow (1929–37) MA, BSc, PhD; St John's College, Cambridge (1937–9) PhD. Royal Aircraft Establishment (1939–40). Ministry of Aircraft Production and Ministry of Supply (1940–4). Manhattan Project, Berkeley (1944–5). Senior Lecturer, University of Glasgow (1946–54). Chief Scientist, UKAEA (Aldermaston and Harwell) (1955–9). Principal, Royal College of Science and Technology, Glasgow (1960–4). Principal and Vice-Chancellor, Strathclyde University (1964–80). Now Visiting Professor, Energy Studies, University of Glasgow.
Publications include: 1979 (With J S Curran) *Energy and Human Needs* (Edinburgh: Scottish Academic)

Professor R W Ditchburn FRS, FInstP, MIA (b. 1903)
Bootle Secondary School; University of Liverpool (1919–22) BSc; Trinity College, Cambridge (1922–8) BA, PhD. Fellow, Trinity College, Dublin (1928–46). Professor of Natural and Experimental Philosophy, Dublin, (1929–46). Professor of Physics, University of Reading (1946–68). Now Emeritus Professor.
Publications include: 1973 *Eye Movements and Visual Perception*
1976 *Light* (New York: Academic)

Professor H Fröhlich FRS (b. 1905)
University of Munich (1927–30) DPhil. *Privatdozent* (Lecturer), University of Freiburg. Research Physicist, Lecturer, Reader (Theoretical Physics), University of Bristol (1935–48). Professor of Theoretical Physics, University of Liverpool (1948–73). Now Emeritus Professor. Professor of Solid State Electronics (1973–6), Visiting Fellow (1976–81), University of Salford. Foreign Member, Max Planck Institut, Stuttgart (1980).

Lady Jeffreys (née B Swirles) (b. 1903)
Northampton School for Girls; Girton College, Cambridge (1921-8)
BA, PhD. Assistant Lecturer, Applied Mathematics, Manchester,
Bristol, Imperial College (1928-33). Lecturer, University of Manchester
(1933-8). Staff Fellow and Tutor, Mathematics, Girton College
(1938-69). Now Fellow.
Publications include: 1946 (With Sir Harold Jeffreys) *Methods of*
Mathematical Physics (Cambridge: Cambridge
University Press)
1977 ed. *Collected Papers of Sir Harold Jeffreys*
(New York: Gordon and Breach)

Professor R V Jones CB, CBE, FRS (b. 1911)
Alleyn's School; Wadham College, Oxford (1929-34) MA, DPhil.
Senior Student in Astronomy, Balliol College, Oxford (1934-6). Scientific Officer, Air Ministry (1936-8), seconded to Admiralty (1938-9).
Air Staff (1939). Assistant Director of Intelligence (1941), Director
(1946). Director, Scientific Intelligence, Ministry of Defence (1952-3).
Professor of Natural Philosophy, University of Aberdeen (1946-81).
Now Emeritus Professor.
Publications include: 1978 *Most Secret War* (London: Hamish
Hamilton)

Professor N Kurti CBE, FRS, FInstP (b. 1908)
Minta Gymnasium, Budapest; Sorbonne (1926-8) L ès Sc, University of
Berlin (1928-31) DrPhil. Research Assistant, Technische Hochschule,
Breslau (1931-33), Clarendon Laboratory, Oxford (1933-40). Tube
Alloys (1940-45). Demonstrator, Reader and Professor, University of
Oxford (1967-75). Fellow Brazenose College.

Professor H S Lipson CBE, FRS, FInstP (b. 1910)
Hawarden Grammar; University of Liverpool (1927-31) MSc, DSc
(1939). University of Liverpool, University of Manchester (1936). NPL
(1937). University of Cambridge (1938). Head of Physics Department,
Manchester College of Technology (1945). Professor of Physics, UMIST
(1954-77). Now Emeritus.
Publications include: 1981 (With S G Lipson) *Optical Physics* (Cambridge: Cambridge University Press)
1984 *Study of Metals and Alloys by X-Ray*
Powder Diffraction Methods (Cardiff: University College, Cardiff Press)

Professor Sir Bernard Lovell OBE, FRS (b. 1913)
Kingswood School, Bristol; University of Bristol (1931-6) BSc, PhD.
Principal Officer, Telecommunications Research Establishment

(1939–45). Assistant Lecturer, Lecturer, Senior Lecturer, Reader, Professor of Radio Astronomy, University of Manchester (1936–81). Director, Nuffield Radio Astronomy Laboratories (1951–81).
Publications include: 1968 *Story of Jodrell Bank*
                  1980 *In the Centre of Immensities* (London: Paladin)
                  1985 *Emerging Cosmology* (Eastbourne: Praeger)

Professor Sir William McCrea FRS, FRSE, FRAS, MRIA (b. 1904)
Chesterfield Grammar School; Trinity College, Cambridge (1923–6) BA. Lecturer in Mathematics, University of Edinburgh (1930–2). Reader, Assistant Professor of Mathematics, Imperial College, London (1932–6). Professor of Mathematics, Queens University, Belfast (1936–44). Professor of Mathematics, Royal Holloway College, London (1944–6). Professor of Theoretical Astronomy, University of Sussex (1966–72). Now Emeritus.
Publications include: 1957 *Relativity Physics* (London: Methuen)

Professor G C McVittie OBE, FRSE (b. 1904)
University of Edinburgh (1923–7) MA; Christ College, Cambridge (1927–30) PhD. Assistant Lecturer, Leeds University (1930–4). Lecturer, Applied Mathematics, University of Liverpool (1934–6). Reader, Applied Mathematics, Kings College, London (1936–48). Professor of Mathematics, Queen Mary College, London (1948–52). Professor of Astronomy, University of Illinois (1952–72). Planet named after him in 1984.
Publications include: 1937 *Cosmological theory*
                  1956 *General Relativity and Cosmology*
                  1961 *Fact and Theory in Cosmology*

Professor Sir Nevill Mott FRS, FInstP (b. 1905)
Clifton College, Bristol; St. John's College, Cambridge (1924–7) BA. Lecturer in Mathematical Physics, University of Manchester (1929–30). Lecturer, University of Cambridge (1930–3). Professor of Theoretical Physics, University of Bristol (1933), H H Wills Professor and Director H H Wills Laboratory (1948–54). Master, Gonville and Caius College, Cambridge (1950–66). Cavendish Professor (1954–71). Nobel Prize, Physics (1977).
Publications include: 1972 *Elementary Quantum Mechanics* (London: Wykeham)
                  1974 *Metal–insulator Transitions* (London: Taylor and Francis)
                  1979 (With E A Davis) *Electronic Processes in Non-crystalline Materials* (Oxford: Oxford University Press)

Professor D Shoenberg FRS, MBE (b. 1911)
Latymer Upper School, London; Trinity College, Cambridge (1929–35)
BA, PhD. Senior Student (1936–9). Lecturer, Reader, Professor,
University of Cambridge (1944–78), In charge Mond Laboratory
(1947–73).
Publications include: 1952 *Superconductivity* (Cambridge: Cambridge
University Press)
1949 *Magnetism* (London: Sigma)

Professor E T S Walton (b. 1903)
Methodist College, Belfast; Trinity College, Dublin (1922–6) BA,
Cavendish Laboratory, Cambridge (1927–31) PhD. Fellow, Trinity
College, Dublin (1934–74), Erasmus Smith Professor of Natural
Philosophy (1946), Senior Fellow, Trinity College, Dublin (1960).
Nobel Prize, Physics, with J D Cockcroft (1951).

Dr F A B Ward CBE (b. 1905)
Highgate School, London; Sydney Sussex College, Cambridge
(1924–31) BA, PhD. Assistant Keeper, Science Museum, London
(1931–9). Seconded to Air Ministry (1939–45). Keeper, Department of
Physics, Science Museum, London (1945–70).
Publications include: 1981 ed. *Catalogue of European Scientific Instru-
ments* (London: British Museum Publications)
1975 ed. *Planetarium of Giovanni De Dondi
Citizen of Padua* (Wadhurst: Antiquarian
Horological Society)

Professor J G Wilson (b. 1911)
Hartlepool Secondary School, County Durham; Sydney Sussex College,
Cambridge (1929–36) BA, PhD. Lecturer, Reader, University of Man-
chester (1938–52). Cavendish Professor, University of Leeds (1963–76).
Now Emeritus.
Publications include: 1976 *Cosmic Rays* (London: Wykeham)

APPENDIX TWO

NOTES AND REFERENCES ON THE INSTITUTIONS

ENGLAND

Bristol

University College, Bristol, was founded in 1876. Silvanus P Thompson (1851–1916) was the first Professor of Physics. The College was one of the more poorly endowed University Colleges in England. A gift of £100 000 from the tobacco millionaire H O Wills doubled the endowment fund and enabled the College to obtain a university charter in 1909, merging with the Merchant Venturer's College. The first research student had come to the college in 1893. Arthur M Tyndall (1881–1961), who had been a student in the College in 1898 and later a lecturer, headed the department from 1910. In 1919 he was appointed H O Wills Professor of Physics. The Wills family endowed £200 000 for a new physics laboratory; when it opened in 1927 it was the most palatial in the country. The department acquired a second chair when J E Lennard-Jones (1894–1954) became Professor of Theoretical Physics in the same year. Tyndall was the Director of the H H Wills Laboratory from 1927 to 1948. The number of students studying physics had increased from 55 in 1917 to over 272 in 1919, falling to 60 in 1937–8. The Honours school remained small, never exceeding six. The number of research workers, however, increased from 13 in 1928 to over 30 in 1939.

References

Cottle B and Sherborne J W 1951 *The Life of a University* (Bristol)
Keith S T 1984 Scientists as Entrepreneurs: Arthur Tyndall and the Rise of Bristol Physics *Ann. Sci.* **41** 335–57

Bristol University Library Archives *Tyndall Papers* files DM 219, 253, 362–5

The University of Bristol: New Physics Laboratory 1927 *Nature* **120** 601–2

Cambridge

The year 1822 marked the beginning of a period of reform which in the space of sixty years transformed the educational system in Cambridge. The system of examination by disputation in Latin, which had prevailed from medieval times and was used to place candidates into classes of 'wranglers', 'senior and junior optimes' and 'poll men', prior to an examination in the Senate House (since 1730), was completely replaced by written examinations. (The last Latin disputations were held in 1839.) Printed papers were used for the first time in 1827 in the Senate House examination. The examination for the Ordinary degree was effectively separated from that for Honours at this time. A previous examination, later known as 'little-go', to be taken by all degree candidates in the fifth term of residence, was instituted in 1822; this eventually became the university entrance examination. Compulsory Greek was abolished from it in 1919. In 1846 the examination for Honours men, now known as the Mathematical Tripos, was divided into two parts. A Board of Mathematical Studies was set up. The Natural Sciences Tripos was instituted in 1851. The subjects included chemistry, geology, mineralogy, botany, zoology, comparative anatomy and comparative physiology. 'So much general physics as is necessary to the right understanding of chemical processes' was taught under chemistry. In 1860 the Senate agreed to grant BA degrees to men with three years residence who had passed the Tripos examinations with Honours. The Natural Sciences Tripos was divided into two parts on the model of the Mathematical Tripos and a practical examination lasting over two days was introduced in 1872. It was also recognised that 'the amount of Physics now included in the subjects of examination was so large as to make it impossible to treat it any longer as an appendage to the examination in Chemistry'. By 1882 the Board of Natural Science Studies had separated into two boards, one of Physical and Chemical Studies and the other of Biological and Geological Studies. Twelve new Chairs were founded between 1851 and 1882, including the Cavendish Professorship of Experimental Physics. James Clerk Maxwell (1831–79) was the first occupant of this Chair from 1871 to 1879, he was succeeded by Lord Rayleigh, who occupied the Chair from 1879 to 1884, J J Thomson from 1884 to 1919 and Lord Rutherford from 1919 to 1937. The Cavendish Laboratory was completely built by a donation from the

Seventh Duke of Devonshire (family name Cavendish); it opened in 1874 and systematic undergraduate laboratory instruction began in 1879. Practical notebooks signed by a teacher were brought into the examination in 1898; no marks were assigned to them, but by looking at the year's work the examiners 'should be thereby enabled to form a more adequate opinion of the merit of the candidates as regards practical work'. Mathematical (Hons) Tripos students were allowed to study for Part II of the Natural Sciences Tripos. A research degree for graduates of other universities was introduced in 1895; the first to arrive under this scheme were Rutherford and Townsend. Teaching of undergraduates was undertaken by the Fellows of the Colleges and the University professors. Religious tests for students were abolished in 1856 and for teaching posts in 1871. Except for the introduction of Faculties in the 1920s, the organisation of teaching and examination has remained the same to this day. In the inter-war period the Cavendish was pre-eminent in attracting students and overseas researchers.

References

Crowther J G 1974 *The Cavendish Laboratory, 1874–1974* (London: Macmillan)
Hilkin T J N 1967 *Engineering at Cambridge University 1783–1965* (Cambridge: Cambridge University Press)
Winstanley D A 1940 *Early Victorian Cambridge* (Cambridge)
—— 1947 *Later Victorian Cambridge* (Cambridge)
Biographies of Lord Rutherford and J J Thomson *see Appendix 3*
Cambridge University Library Archives *Minutes of the Board of Physical and Chemical Studies* UA MinV/83
—— *Cambridge University Register* CUR 28.9

Liverpool

University College, Liverpool, was founded in 1881, becoming a constituent college of the Victoria University in 1884. In 1903 it became the independent University of Liverpool. Oliver Lodge (1851–1940) was appointed to the Lyon Jones Chair of Experimental Physics and Mathematics in 1881 (the title changed to Experimental Physics in 1882, and to Physics from 1900). Lionel Robert Wilberforce (1861–1944) occupied the Chair from 1900 until his retirement in 1935. He excelled at lecture demonstrations; a large stock of apparatus left behind by him was used readily by his successors. James Rice (1874–1936) was a Senior Lecturer from 1914, Associate Professor from 1924 and Reader in theoretical physics from 1935. He was one of the early expositors of the theory of relativity. The George Holt Laboratory, endowed with a gift of £10 000 by the Holt family, was opened in 1904. It was in the special x-ray room of this laboratory that Barkla demonstrated the polarisation of x-rays. The number of physics students was small. For example, in 1921-2 there were 12; in contrast, chemistry had 224, engineering 324 and medicine 839. (These numbers, which had been inflated by ex-servicemen, declined subsequently.) James Chadwick (1891-1974) on his appointment to the Chair in 1935 started the construction of the 37" cyclotron, which came into operation in 1939. University College, Liverpool, was the first academic body in England to establish a Students' Representative Council, which became the University's Guild of Undergraduates.

References

Kelly T 1981 *For Advancement of Learning: the University of Liverpool 1881-1981* (Liverpool: Liverpool University Press)
Wilberforce L R 1928 *The University of Liverpool 1903-1928, A Brief Record of Work in Progress* (University of Liverpool)
Liverpool University Archives *Annual Reports*
Liverpool University New Buildings: the Physics Laboratory *Manchester Guardian* 12 Nov 1904; 1904 *Nature* **71** 63-5

Manchester

Owens College, Manchester, was founded in 1851 with a bequest amounting to £96 654 from the Manchester businessman John Owens to provide higher education for men, without constraints of religious tests. It was the only institution in England, outside London, which provided systematic scientific education. Students were awarded a Diploma of Associateship of the College, which prepared them for matriculation for London degrees and for entry to Oxford or Cambridge. The Dalton Scholarships in Science, instituted in 1856, were the first for original research. The first practical classes were provided in the session 1870-1 by Balfour Stewart (1828-87). The teaching included mathematical and theoretical physics from as early as 1862. The federal Victoria University received its charter in 1880, Owens College becoming its first, and for a time its only, constituent college. University College, Liverpool, and Yorkshire College, Leeds, joined in 1884 and 1887 respectively. The independent Victoria University of Manchester came into being in 1903. (Liverpool and Leeds too acquired university status.)

When the new Physical Laboratories opened in 1900 they were the fourth largest in the world, after Johns Hopkins, Darmstadt and Strasbourg. Professors included Robert B Clifton (1860–6) and Balfour Stewart (1870–87) in Natural Philosophy and Arthur Schuster (1888–1907), Ernest Rutherford (1907–19), W L Bragg (1919–37) and P M S Blackett (1937–53) as Langworthy Professors of Physics. Manchester was one of the larger physics departments, e.g. the number of students in the third year Honours class for the years 1929 and 1936 were 19 and 17 respectively. It was also prolific in publications.

References

Charlton H B 1951 *Portrait of a University 1851–1951* (Manchester: Manchester University Press)
Harker J R 1907 *Nature* **76** 640–2
——1912 *Nature* **89** 46
Thompson J 1886 *Owens College, its Foundation and Growth* (Manchester)
Thomson J J 1936 *Recollections and Reflections* (London: Bell) ch.1
Manchester University Library Archives *Calendars* UA/19–21; *Reports of the Council* UA/22–3
1898 The New Physical Laboratories *Nature* **58** 621
1906 *The Physical Laboratories of the University of Manchester* (Manchester)

Oxford

A Readership in Experimental Philosophy had existed since 1749. Robert Walker had been a Reader since 1839 and became the first Professor of Experimental Philosophy in 1860 when the post was raised to a Professorship. The New Museum, with its splendid Radcliffe Scientific Library, opened in 1860 and the School of Natural Science was also founded in that year. Lectures and practical classes (which were made 'an absolute necessity for a degree in the Natural Science School') were held at the Museum as well as at the colleges, some of which possessed laboratories, scientific specimens and apparatus. The subjects taught included chemistry, physics (heat, light, electricity) and mechanics, physiology, botany, zoology, geology and mineralogy. R B Clifton (1836–1921) occupied the Chair of Experimental Philosophy from 1865 to 1915. The Clarendon Laboratory was opened in 1870. It was financed from the proceeds of the sale of the Earl of Clarendon's *History of the*

Great Rebellion. The collection of apparatus was considered very valuable, having come from the Paris Exhibition of 1867.

In 1901 J S E Townsend (1868–1957) became the first holder of the newly founded Wykeham Chair of Experimental Physics. Statutes were changed to divide the teaching between the two Chairs: mechanics, heat, light and sound were allocated to Experimental Philosophy, and electricity and magnetism to the Wykeham Professor. The new Electrical Laboratory for Townsend was opened in 1910, with a donation of £ 23 000 from the Worshipful Company of Drapers. F A Lindemann (1886–1957) was appointed to the Chair of Experimental Philosophy in 1919; the title was changed in 1921 and he became Dr Lee's Professor of Experimental Physics. In 1919 the Clarendon Laboratory was in poor condition, with no mains electricity and only gas lighting. The building was soon modernised, and Lindemann did much to acquire new equipment and resources. Between 1919 and 1939 the research and academic staff increased from 2 to 20, technical staff from 1 to 5 and the intake of undergraduates from 6 to 25. The Laboratory became distinguished in low-temperature research and spectroscopy with the arrival, through Lindemann's efforts, of emigré scientists like Simon, Mendelssohn, Kurti and Kuhn from Germany in the 1930s. The new Clarendon Laboratory opened in 1939 and new Fellowships were created. The Wykeham Chair was converted to Theoretical Physics on Townsend's retirement in 1941, leaving all experimental work to the Dr Lee's Professor.

References

Earwaken J P 1870 Natural Science at Oxford *Nature* **3** 170
See F A Lindemann and J S E Townsend, Appendix 3

Sheffield

The University of Sheffield received its charter in 1905. It was constituted around the nucleus of the Firth College, which was founded in 1879 by a donation amounting to £ 39 000 from M Firth, a wealthy ironmaster. The Medical College, founded in 1828, and the People's College (1842) became integral parts of the University, the latter forming the basis of the Arts faculty. Mathematics and physics existed as one department until 1892. W M Hicks (1850–1934) was the first head of the physics department from 1892 to 1917, and the first Vice-Chancellor of the University. S R Milner (1875–1958), who had been educated at

University College, Bristol, and at Nernst's Physical Institute in Göttingen, was appointed lecturer in 1900 and was Professor from 1921 to 1940. The Honours school was small, varying between one and seven students in the period 1920–34.

References

Chapman A W 1955 *The Story of a Modern University. A History of the University of Sheffield* (Oxford: Oxford University Press)
University Calendars

IRELAND

Trinity College, Dublin

See Professor Walton's essay, Capter 4.

Reference

McDowell R B and Webb D A 1982 *Trinity College Dublin 1592–1952, An Academic History* (Cambridge: Cambridge University Press)

SCOTLAND

The dates of foundation of the four ancient universities were as follows: St Andrews (1410), Glasgow (1451), Aberdeen (1494) and Edinburgh (1583). They were to a much greater extent than those in England, the universities of the people. The conditions of the universities slowly improved during the eighteenth century; the regenting system and the use of Latin for lecturing gradually disappeared; the century marked a brilliant period of intellectual life in Scotland. There were no entrance examinations, students entered very young and selected their own subject of study; the majority did not proceed to a degree. The University (Scotland) Act of 1858 reconstructed the government of the university; graduates were included on the council. At Edinburgh the patronage was transferred from the town council to the curators, some to be elected by the University Court. The degree of MA, to be taken in three stages, replaced the BA as the first degree. A Preliminary Examination for university entrance was enforced in 1892. The Argyll Commission (1867) on schools, which became the Education (Scotland)

Act in 1872, was more comprehensive and far-reaching than its English counterpart. It was effectively the Newcastle, Clarendon and Taunton Commissions rolled into one. One of its consequences was the substitution of state for church control in education. The Leaving Certificate Examination, administered by the Education Department, was introduced in 1888. This was accepted as an entrance qualification by many bodies. This was a quarter of a century ahead of the English School Certificate Examination, which was conducted by the universities.

Glasgow

The Professorship of Natural Philosophy was founded in 1577. Lord Kelvin (1824–1907) occupied the Chair from 1846 to 1899. Due to his early interest in electrical telegraphy, he established a laboratory in 1852 in an unused wine cellar near his lecture room. The new buildings of the University of 1870 provided considerable space for Experimental Natural Philosophy. Andrew Gray succeeded Lord Kelvin and continued until 1924. He was an authority on gyroscopes. The new Department of Natural Philosophy was completed in 1907, with the help of the Carnegie Trust. A H.Wilson headed the department until 1926 and was succeeded by E Taylor Jones (1872–1961), who held the Chair until 1943. Through a large part of this period, James Gray was in the associated Chair of Applied Mathematics, followed by Thomas Alty.

References

Bottomly J T 1872 Physical Science at Glasgow *Nature* **6** 29–32
Coutts J 1909 *The History of the University of Glasgow* (Glasgow)
Gray A 1897 *Nature* **55** 486–92
Thompson S P 1910 *The Life of William Thomson, Baron Kelvin of Largs* (London)

Edinburgh

The Chair of Natural Philosophy was instituted in 1583. The professors included James D Forbes (1809–78), who held the Chair from 1833 to 1860; he was succeeded by Peter G Tait (1831–1901), who occupied the Chair until his death. The physics laboratory was organised by Tait in 1868. He was followed by James G MacGregor from 1901 to 1913. The department moved into new buildings in 1907–8. C G Barkla (1877–1944) held the Chair from 1913 until his death. C G Darwin

(1887–1962) occupied the Tait Chair of Natural Philosophy, which was ostensibly of Mathematical Physics, from 1923 to 1936.

References

Grant A 1884 *The Story of the University of Edinburgh, first 300 years* (London)

Horn D B 1967 *A Short History of the University of Edinburgh, 1556–1889* (Edinburgh)

Turner L ed. 1933 *History of the University of Edinburgh 1883–1933* (Edinburgh: Oliver and Boyd)

Edinburgh University Library *Calendars*; *University of Edinburgh Journal*

APPENDIX THREE

PERSONALIA–SOURCES OF INFORMATION

Sources include biographies and obituaries. *ON* and *BM* refer to the *Obituary Notices of Fellows of the Royal Society* and to the *Biographical Memoirs of the Fellows of the Royal Society* respectively. For a fuller bibliography of sources, see J L Heilbron and B R Wheaton *Literature on the History of Physics in the 20th Century*, 1981 (cited below as *LHP*).

Aston F W(1877–1945)	*ON* **5**(1945–48) 635–51
Barkla C G(1877–1944)	*ON* **5**(1947) 341–66
	LHP 326
Blackett P M S(1897–1974)	*BM* **21**(1975) 1–115
Bohr N(1885–1962)	French A P and Kennedy P J eds. 1985 *A Centenary Volume* (Cambridge, MA: Harvard University Press)
	BM **9**(1963) 37–53
	LHP 31–35
Bragg W L(1890–1971)	*BM* **25**(1979) 75–143
Chadwick J(1891–1974)	*BM* **22**(1976) 11–70
Cockcroft J D(1897–1967)	*BM* **14**(1968) 139–88
	Hartcup G and Allibone T E 1984 *Cockcroft and the Atom* (Bristol: Adam Hilger)
Cotton A A (1869–1953)	*Académie des Sciences Notices et discours* **3**(1953) 448–77
	Cotton E 1967 *Aimé Cotton* (Paris)
Darwin C G(1887–1962)	*BM* **9**(1963) 69–85

Dirac P A M(1902–84)

BM **32** (1986) 137
Salam A and Wigner E P eds. 1972
Aspects of quantum theory
(Cambridge: Cambridge University
Press)

Eddington A S(1882–1944)

ON **5**(1945) 113–25
Douglas A V 1956 *The life of Arthur
Stanley Eddington*

Ellis C D(1895–1980)

BM **27**(1981) 199–234

Fabry Ch(1867–1945)

ON **5**(1945–48) 445–50
Académie des Sciences Mémoires
67(1946) 27

Fowler R H(1889–1944)

ON **5**(1945) 61–78

Hartree D R(1897–1958)

BM **4**(1958) 103–16

Kapitza P L(1894–1984)

BM **31**(1985) 327–73

Lindemann F A
(1886–1957)

BM **4**(1958) 45–71
Earl of Birkenhead 1961 *The Prof. in
two Worlds* (London: Collins)

Milner S R(1875–1958)

BM **5**(1959) 129–47

Nicholson J W(1881–1955)

BM **2**(1956) 209–14

Oliphant M
(b. Adelaide 1901)

Cockburn S and Ellyard D 1981
Oliphant, Life and Times

Ratcliffe J A (b. 1902)

Sidney Sussex College, Cambridge,
Fellow (1927–60). Reader, University
of Cambridge (1947–60). War service,
TRE Malvern. President, Physical
Society (1959–60).

Rutherford E(1871–1937)

Eve A S 1939 *Rutherford: Being the
life and letters of the Rt. Hon. Lord
Rutherford OM* (New York)
Wilson D H 1983 *Rutherford*
(London: Hodder and Stoughton)
LHP 200–5

Searle G F C(1864–1954)

BM **1**(1955) 247–52
Woodall A J and Hawkins A C 1969
Laboratory Physics and its debt to
G F C Searle *Phys. Ed.* **4** 283–5

Skinner H W B(1900–60)

BM **6**(1960) 259–68

Sommerfeld A J W
(1868–1951)

ON **8**(1952) 275–96
LHP 215–16

Taylor G I(1886–1975)

BM **22**(1976) 565–633

Taylor-Jones E(1872–1961)

Curran, Sir Samuel 1961 *Nature* **192**
605

Thirkill H (1886–1971)

Tutor, President, Master, Clare College, Cambridge (1920–58), Vice-Chancellor, University of Cambridge (1945–7).

Thomson J J(1856–1940)

Strutt R J 1943 *The Life of Sir J J Thomson, OM, sometime master of Trinity College, Cambridge* (Cambridge: Cambridge University Press)
Thomson J J 1936 *Recollections and Reflections* (London: Bell)
LHP 225–6

Townsend J S E (1868–1957)

BM 3(1957) 257–72

Tyndall A M(1881–1961)

BM 8(1962) 159–65

Wien W C(1864–1928)

Naturwiss. 17(1929) 675–681

Whittaker E T(1873–1956)

BM 2(1956) 299–325 1957 *J. Lon. Math. Soc.* 32 234–56
Hardie C D 1943 *Isis* 34 344–6

Wilson C T R(1869–1950)

BM 6(1960) 269–95
Reminiscences of my early years *Not. Rec. R. Soc.* 14(1960) 163–73

Wilberforce L R (1861–1944)

Roberts R W 1944 *Nature* 153 517
Wood A B 1945 *Proc. Phys. Soc.* 57 585

INDEX